6

HX

THE LOVE-LIFE OF ANIMALS

by

WOLFGANG VON BUDDENBROCK

Translated from the German by

J. M. CHAPLIN

FREDERICK MULLER LTD
LONDON

PRINTED AND BOUND IN GREAT BRITAIN BY
THE GARDEN CITY PRESS LIMITED
LETCHWORTH, HERTFORDSHIRE

COPYRIGHT, 1956, FREDERICK MULLER LTD.

CONTENTS

LIST OF PLATES

FOREWORD

THE aim of the present book is to make available to a wider public the fascinating field of the courtship and mating of animals. It is therefore not a learned book and makes no claim to be counted among the strictly professional scientific literature. Nevertheless the author has been at pains to keep it abreast of the most modern scientific thought, and he hopes that the book will give the student of biology a condensed survey of this interesting chapter of knowledge.

Since this book seeks thus to appeal to two different classes of readers, the author must beg that each category will have a little consideration for the other. The educated layman may forgive a series of perhaps incomprehensible scientific expressions and indigestible Latin names, intended for the student of biology, which do not, however, diminish the ease of reading the text. Finally, then, I crave pardon for numerous anthropomorphisms, used only to make the narrative flow more readily.

The assembling of my material has been made considerably more easy by the friendly aid of a number of young naturalists in our institute. Here I would thank Messrs. Thomas, Nicolai, Kinkel, Pabst, Weil, Pauly and Sturm for many inspirations and the use of their newest discoveries. I would thank Miss Eva von Schlieben for the laborious preparation of the many text figures. To the publisher is due my sincere gratitude for the excellent production and the provision of numerous illustrations.

W. v. BUDDENBROCK.

INTRODUCTION

THE living garment which covers Mother Earth like a delicate bloom is subject to constant change. The old withers, and young life gushes forth endlessly to repeat it. This life is not created by mysterious powers, the so-called spontaneous generation, but by beings of the same species uniting and giving their reproductive cells the opportunity to do likewise. Looked at without prejudice and without the standards of value which we humans apply to all earthly matters, these things, however frail they may be and no matter how secretly they may take place, are the most important in the world, for without them there would be absolutely no life on earth. It is perhaps rewarding therefore to spend a few hours studying this question.

Science places everything belonging to this subject under the name of the biology of sex. This is a subject with which one could fill many volumes, but it is easy to divide the immense mass into two parts. The first part comprises all that can be said of the reproductive cells, the ova and the spermatozoa. Here there are a thousand mysterious things with which are associated the most difficult problems in biology. We can only go as far with these in this small book as will be absolutely necessary for an understanding of the further discussion. It is the second part which will chiefly occupy our attention, and which is concerned with the activities of adult animals in propagating their species, and these activities, may, as the title of the book suggests, be summarized as "the love-life of animals".

When we use this phrase we must not, of course, apply too human an interpretation. In human beings it is the mind that imparts to love its ethical values and is the reason why poets in all languages take it as their theme in endless variation. If now we turn to the beasts, we descend, with a few rare exceptions, from these radiant heights to the murky depths of the lower regions of impulsive life in which ethics have no part. On the other hand, other mysteries of love will confront us and much of this will appear in a new light.

PART ONE

Meeting and Mating

I

THE FERTILIZATION OF THE OVUM

THE world of living things is governed by one great law. Nature compels its creatures to carry out actions of which the final results remain completely unknown to them. This it achieves by holding out a bait towards which, thanks to their desires, they strive greedily.

For animals the satisfaction of this desire is their highest aim in life, but for Nature it is a means to a much higher end, and which remains concealed from the creature itself. When a nagging hunger torments us we seek to fill our stomachs, and at the same time we enjoy the taste of the food. But whilst we are doing this we are certainly not thinking that the taking of food serves for the assimilation of so many calories, without which we could not live.

With love the case is the same, and Schiller's immortal words "Meanwhile whilst world philosophy persists, the wheels will turn through hunger and through love", are today as true as on the day they were first written. Lovers yearn for their union with great emotion and regard it as the greatest happiness on earth, but no beast, and also no primitive man, had the slightest notion of its consequences. Civilized man, it is true, knows that from the union of two lovers a joyous event will take place, but how in detail this comes about was entirely unknown until not so very long ago. Astonishing as it may sound, it is only since the year 1875 that we have known about this most profound mystery of life. Since that year, however, we have known for certain that the meaning of all the emotion of love and the rapture is that deep inside the female body a very subtle process has taken place, namely the combination of two reproductive cells, the ovum and the spermatozoon.

The spermatozoa, which in all animals look much alike, were first discovered at the end of the seventeenth century (1667) by the famous Dutch naturalist Leeuwenhoek, but at first nobody knew what to do with this knowledge. That all animals, including Man, produce eggs and that this is not solely a peculiarity of birds and fish was not understood until much later. The egg of mammals was not discovered until 1827, but the relation between the eggs and the spermatozoa was unknown to anyone in the world before 1875. Leeuwenhoek, with the

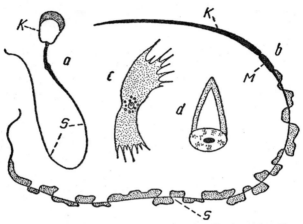

FIG. 1. Spermatozoa of various animals: (*a*) guinea-pig; (*b*) salamander; (*c*) crustacean, *Sida cristallina*; (*d*) roundworm.

intuition of a great naturalist, had already asserted that the spermatozoon must penetrate into the egg. Later, other microscopists had found the tail of a spermatozoon in the plasma of a fertilized egg. But farther than this no one had progressed.

Nevertheless our knowledge had been greatly enriched meanwhile. Theodor Schwann had in 1839 propounded the thesis that our entire organism is composed of innumerable microscopically small cells which are therefore the stuff of which our bodies are composed. Each cell is an infinitely small sphere consisting of the remarkable living substance known as protoplasm, and which contains a nucleus. As soon as this had been established, it became clear to those with eyes to see it that the egg and spermatozoon were themselves nothing but cells.

Discovery had reached this point when Oskar Hertwig, a pupil of Ernst Haeckel, commenced to work on this problem. The reproductive cells of the higher animals are most unsuitable for these studies, so it was

PLATE I.

Dynastes hercules. Hercules beetle.
Left male, right female.

Xylotrupes dichotomus. Male left, female right.

Banded Newt (*Triturus vittatus*) from Asia Minor in his wedding garment.

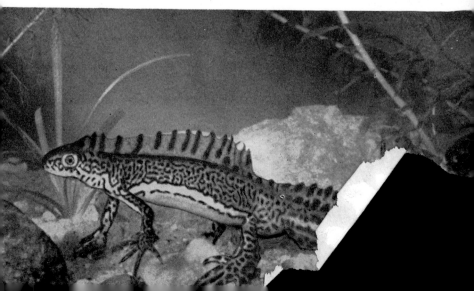

PLATE II.

Sacred baboon or hamadryad; the male on the left, the female on the right.

PLATE III.
Amorous elephant couple at the Berlin Zoo.

PLATE IV.
Penguin feeding its young.

necessary to turn to simpler forms of life in which everything is clearer and less complicated. Hertwig found an eminently suitable subject in the sea-urchin. Its eggs, which it produces by the thousand, are tiny crystal-clear globules which can be kept alive for a long time in clean sea-water. The small spermatozoa can also be preserved in a bowl of sea-

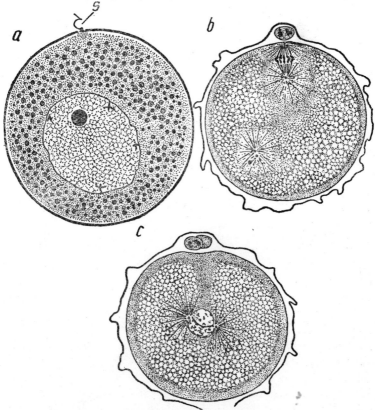

FIG. 2. Fertilization of the egg cells of the *Urechis caupo* worm: (*a*) penetration by the spermatozoon, in the middle of the egg the very large nucleus; (*b*) formation of the second polar body of ovum. Both nuclei are surrounded by an aster, sperm nucleus below left, ovum nucleus above; (*c*) Both nuclei have combined but are still separated by a ridge.

water, where their wriggling can be watched. If, now, one isolates an egg to examine it more precisely under the microscope, and adds a trace of seminal fluid, it will immediately become apparent that an incredible swarm of spermatozoa congregates around it, drawn there by a powerful attraction from the egg. One only will reach its goal, however, and manage to penetrate into the egg. This observation was by itself no great advance. Hertwig, nevertheless, was able to proceed very much farther by careful observations which convinced him that the final and most important part was the union of the male and female nucleus.

Hertwig could not in his time know the extreme importance of his

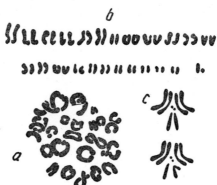

FIG. 3. Chromosomes: (*a*) diploid (double) set of chromosomes in Man; (*b*) the same arranged in pairs of chromosomes; (*c*) set of chromosomes of a fly, *Drosophila*, (*above*) female, (*below*) male.

discovery. Since then the heirs to the fruits of his knowledge have followed successfully in the path he indicated. We know now that the nucleus is the bearer of all our inherited propensities. In it are the chromosomes, fixed in number for each species of animal. The total of the chromosomes in a nucleus is called a set of chromosomes. In a careful drawing of a set of chromosomes it can be shown that not all chromosomes are alike; one may be long and threadlike, another short and thick, while yet others may be spherical, and so on. Further, one can determine with certainty that each chromosome is duplicated, and, to cut a long story short, it can be said that one of each pair comes from the father and one from the mother.

The nuclei of the reproductive cells, ovum and spermatozoon, undergo a remarkable preparation before they unite in this action we call fertilization. The fertilization is preceded by a process known as the maturation or ripening. This maturation is a very complicated process—a difficult one to unravel in detail and one which we cannot go into here. We must, nevertheless, note as a most important fact that during this maturation one half of the chromosome mass is ejected from each cell, so that the matured cells possess only one half of a set. During this maturation the pairs of chromosomes are torn apart with the greatest precision. If, therefore, we could letter the set of chromosomes in an immature cell as AA, BB, CC, DD, the formula for the set in a matured cell will be A, B, C, D. The logic of this process is crystal clear. When after the spermatozoon has penetrated into the ovum and the nuclei of the two unite, then half the set of chromosomes has come from the spermatozoon and half from the ovum. After the union of the nuclei the formula for the chromosomes appears again as AA, BB, CC, DD. Thus, the original normal chromosome set is restored in such a way that half comes from the father and half from the mother.

When we have realized this fully then we have understood the most profound fact connected with mating, and can confidently proceed to our real task. Going back, however, we may also note another point. The great discoveries of Hertwig and his successors have had an enormous influence on our entire civilized life, and one not sufficiently recognized. Only as a result of these discoveries can the relation between man and wife be seen in its true light. For thousands of years the wife had been regarded as the inferior. She, it was thought, brought forth the substance but the man contributed all that was of a higher nature. Now we know that in the act of reproduction both sexes perform an equal task. Each parent contributes precisely one-half of the inheritance of the child. Each individual chromosome of the mother unites with the corresponding chromosome of the father to form a pair. No mathematician could conceive of a more exact instrument to assure complete equality of effort.

In one important particular indeed the female sex is greatly superior. The ovum is more potent than the spermatozoon. Both contain an equal mass of hereditary material, but the ovum has an astonishing capacity to develop, which the spermatozoon lacks. In fact the ovum does not always need, for that purpose, the assistance of the spermatozoon. If a suitable impetus be given, a process of development may begin in the ovum which continues by an almost endless chain-reaction in which each separate process sets off the next, until the formation of the organism is completed. This is the secret of the ovum, which can be confidently regarded as the greatest wonder of the living world.

2

BIOLOGY OF SEX IN PROTOZOA

IF we examine a drop of water taken from a culture of protozoa, we see swarms of the smallest of living creatures in which the whole body consists of single cells only. It is difficult to imagine that even in these animals which stand at the base of the animal kingdom there exists something in common with the nuptial behaviour of the higher beasts. In fact, it was held, erroneously, for a long time that in protozoa all propagation was by a simple asexual division. Nowadays we know, however, that sexuality in unicellular animals is distributed in precisely the same way as in multicellular animals, or metazoa. We can use a very simple test. Since we have seen that in the higher forms of life procreation consists of the union of two cells, we need only see whether a similar fusion takes place in protozoa also, for they too are no more than cells. The answer is not hard to find.

Should we seek the union of two such cells we find there are two different forms of union, copulation and conjugation. In the first, which is very widely distributed, a complete fusion, in fact, takes place between two entirely separate cells and they become completely one, the so-called zygote. In conjugation, which is only found in some of the protozoa known as ciliates, only a temporary and partial fusion occurs, the two cells later separating.

The chief difference between unicellular and multicellular animals is that sexuality in the former has nothing immediately to do with reproduction. Their reproduction, by which two or more cells are formed from one, proceeds always by simple cell division. There are, however, large numbers of unicellular animals which have a complicated life cycle, and in them the sexual processes are a necessary and constantly present feature. We will select one example, namely the life cycle of the malaria parasite. As we know, these dangerous parasites of man infect the red blood corpuscles. The first sporozoid to enter is very small. Soon, however, it increases in size and finally almost fills the blood corpuscle. By repeated subdivision a number of smaller cells are formed which eventually destroy the corpuscle. Each of these can infest a new corpuscle and there repeat the cycle. The whole process is called schizogony. When it has been repeated for some time a change takes place in that some of the sporozoids no longer divide but grow into spherical gametocytes. The further development of these cells does not take place in the human blood, but in the intestine of the malarial

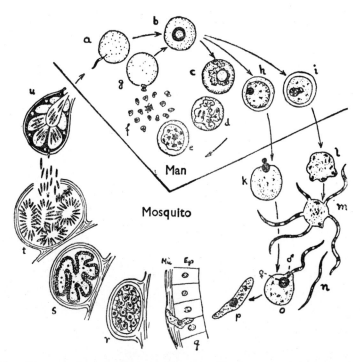

FIG. 4. The cause of malaria—diagram of the chain of development: (*a*) penetration of the germ (sporozoite) into a human red blood corpuscle; (*b*) immature germ becomes circular; (*c*) medium-sized parasite with pseudopodia; (*d*) first segmentation of nucleus; (*e*) segmentation of disintegration (schizogony)—nucleus repeatedly segmented, pigment gathered in the middle; (*f*) destruction of the red blood corpuscle, the germs (merozoites, schizonts) reach the blood fluid; (*g*) attack on a new blood corpuscle by a germ; (*h*) immature female germ (macrogametozoite); (*i*) mother cell of a male immature germ (microgametozoite); *k*) maturing of female germ (macrogamete); (*l*) nuclear segmentation in immature male germ; (*m*) formation of excrescences into which the nuclear masses penetrate, the excrescences become male germs (microgametes); (*n*) mature detached male germ; (*o*) fertilization of a female by a male germ; (*p*) creation of a free fertilized germ (ookinete, zygote); (*q*) the fertilized germ traverses the skin (epithel: Ep) and reaches the muscle layer (Mu) of the same; (*r*) development of spores (sporogony) in the growing parasite (oocyst); (*s*) the protoplasmic body forms processes and involutions on whose surface the newly-created germs (sporozoites) arrange themselves; (*t*) these germs have become spindle-shaped and quit the burst envelope, leaving behind a remainder of unsegmented body. They reach the body fluid of the mosquito in which they spread everywhere; (*u*) they have also penetrated into the salivary gland of the mosquito filling its cells and cavities, and, when the mosquito sucks the blood of a human being, again enter his blood-stream.

mosquito. There two kinds can be recognized: macrogametes which in their appearance and behaviour may be compared to ova, and much smaller microgametes, which arise from subdivision of the original gametocytes and resemble spermatozoa. Now follows a stage which shows that a sexual act is in progress. The microgametes swarm round the macrogametes, in the same way that the spermatozoa surround the ovum, and one of them penetrates the macrogamete to become entirely fused with it. The zygote thus created, which resembles a fertilized ovum, does not immediately commence to subdivide but is transformed first into an elongated and mobile cell which soon passes between the epithelial cells lining the wall of the stomach and into the muscular layer where it becomes spherical. Only now when it has formed a cyst in the intestine, which protrudes outward as a hemispherical lump, does active cell division begin, which finally leads to the formation of numerous new sporozoites. These migrate eventually after the cyst has burst into the salivary gland of the insect and thence easily re-enter the human bloodstream with the bite.

In the malarial parasite the two cells which copulate are markedly dissimilar. We speak of this, therefore, as *anisogamy*. There are, however, many instances in which both partners are superficially alike, so that one is justified in speaking of an *isogamy*. There is, however, reason to believe that a real isogamy does not exist. By using certain vital reagents it is possible to show that the two stain differently. The differentiation into male and female is thus already to be seen at the base of the animal kingdom.

Naturally this does not exhaust the problem. First we have to assume that the cells about to copulate have previously gone through a process of maturation in exactly the same way as the ova and spermatozoa of the metazoa. Actual proof has been obtained in a few cases only, but although our acceptance of this is based largely on theory, it is a conclusion which cannot be avoided. The existence of the process is clearly proved by the so-called autogamy of the *Actinophrys*. Autogamy means self-marriage, and by that we mean the following: When the time comes the individual in question encysts itself, that is, it excretes an outer coat, and within this, for some time, it remains inactive and without feeding. In this cyst very peculiar processes take place. First the cell undergoes simple division. Very soon, however, it can be seen that in each of the two sister cells nuclear division is beginning, in the course of which a part of the nuclear material is extracted. There can be no doubt that we are here dealing with a true maturation division. When it is complete both cells are ready for mating. One throws out grasping processes towards the other, and at the end of the whole proceeding we have again one single animal. That is, one cell, just as at first.

Autogamy provides an opportunity to philosophize a little about the ultimate meaning of sexuality. It might consist in a new combination of chromosomes, that is, in an alteration of the hereditary mass. This is true also of the autogamy of *Actinophrys*. Let us assume an arbitrary number of chromosomes, AA', BB', CC' and DD'. Then, in the maturation division a number of things can happen. It is possible, for instance, that in one cell the chromosomes A', B', CD may be expelled, so that AB, C', D' remain. In the companion cell perhaps A, B'C, D' remain, so that the nuclear fusion of the total chromosome set will assume the formula AA, BB', C'C and D'D', which is materially different from the original one.

Apart from these difficulties the problem of sexuality in protozoa contains another hitherto almost unexplained factor which relates to behaviour, and which we must therefore examine more closely. When the fertilization of the cells has been completed it is obvious that an internal rearrangement has been brought about. The cell which previously concerned itself solely with feeding now shows an overwhelming impulse to unite with another cell. It is obviously attracted by the other, and merely to observe that we are dealing with a chemical attraction is only a small part of the riddle it poses. The primeval, mysterious problem of the relation of male to female is here already, on the threshold of the animal kingdom.

A very different process to copulation is the one we will discuss now, namely conjugation in the ciliates. If we have an old culture of ciliates in which the water has become stagnant so that the animals no longer find optimum conditions for life, we shall see that suddenly a reproductive epidemic breaks out. All the animals come together in pairs, becoming joined by a particular part of the front ends of their bodies. The early microscopists had already observed this in the seventeenth century, but it was usually put down to fighting in which the animals had come to close grips. Only in the nineteenth century, when enough had become known about cells, nuclei and chromosomes, could one approach the solution of this remarkable problem. Now we know that in conjugation as opposed to copulation no complete fusion between two cells takes place, but only an exchange of nuclear material which precedes the usual process of fertilization. Matters are also much complicated because each ciliate possesses two nuclei, a meganucleus and a micronucleus. The meganucleus has by now done its work. It disintegrates and disappears. The micronucleus, on the other hand,

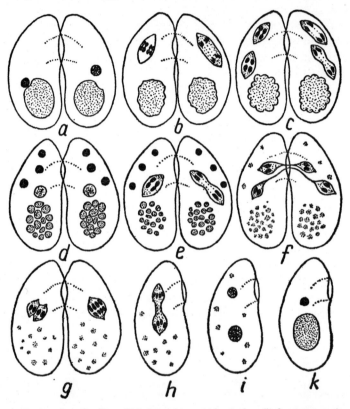

FIG. 5. Conjugation of a ciliate, *Chilodon uncinatus*; (*a*) beginning; (*b*) first segmentation of the micronuclei; (*c*) second segmentation of the micronuclei (reduction-division); (*d*) three micronuclei and the meganucleus perish; (*e*) creation of a stationary and a wandering nucleus; (*f*) exchange of nuclei; (*g*) unification of nuclei; (*h, i, k*) reconstruction of the original condition.

behaves exactly like the nucleus of an ovum in the process of fertilization. It divides twice consecutively so that four nuclei are formed, each of which can be shown to possess only half the number of chromosomes. Strangely enough, three of these nuclei perish. They resemble the polar bodies of an ovum; but these are extruded and are therefore incapable of surviving. Here, on the contrary, we have four nuclei with an equal amount of cell plasma, and for the moment we cannot explain why one survives and the other three perish. We can but note the fact, and in the meanwhile follow the fate of the remaining fourth. It divides again, but without a reduction of chromosomes. And now the most remarkable thing occurs, namely one of the nuclei becomes transferred to the other cell so that at the end each animal has one of its own nuclei and one from its mate. These two nuclei fuse with one another, and with that the proceedings are virtually at an end. The creation of a new meganucleus need not concern us here.

Conjugation does not lead to an increase of the species, and herewith is shown the fundamental difference to the metazoa. There are two cells before and two cells after. But each of these cells has become another by the rejuvenating force of the exchange of nuclei. It can be proved that all life processes which previously had been a little dull and weak experience a renewal of strength: in movement, breathing and also in cell division.

It is interesting that even in ciliates we can see a differentiation between male and female individuals. Among certain colony-building ciliates one may see besides the usual small heads a number of very much smaller ones which acquire on the rear portion of their spherical bodies a circle of cilia, and later, becoming detached, swim away. They seek another colony of the same species of whose readiness for mating they must have become aware in some way or other, and there fuse with a very much larger "female" individual. Incidentally we see here for the first time, and in a very dramatic manner, the "love death". The small male injects his nucleus into the protoplasmic body of the female, so that all that remains of him is a shrivelled scrap which perishes.

3

THE METAZOA

THE protozoa merely provide a prelude. In this book we have to deal with the lives and actions of the multicellular animals, in which the body is composed often of innumerable cells. More important than the number of these cells for the existence of metazoa is the great difference between the germ cells and the body cells which we see in the most varied tissues, skin, bones, muscles and so on. Although the germ cells in most animals lead a very secluded life, they are among the most important of all, for they alone transcend the limits of the mortal individual, they alone throw a bridge across from one generation to the next, they alone represent the continuity of the species.

Their complete meaning was formerly not fully understood. Even in Darwin's day it was believed that the germ cells were under the control of the individual. It was then thought that whatever was achieved by an increased use of the muscles, training the brain by mental exercise or by exerting one's sense organs to the utmost, all this, it was believed, would be communicated in some mysterious way to the germ cells. That is, there was a belief in the inheritance of acquired characters. Modern science has swung sharply away from this conviction. We now believe that the inherited mass is our most valued possession, which by the laws of inheritance goes on from one generation to another, unaltered eternally, as long as no change is caused from within.

The germ cells are the bearers of the inherited mass and thereupon rests their immeasurable value, but the body is only the carrier of the germ cells. It resembles a motor car which is transporting valuables from one bank to another. True, this car has an engine, four wheels, mudguards and a thousand other parts, but all these parts are there only to ensure the safe transport of the valuables. This is their task, and equally it is the task of the metazoan body to bring about the combination of the male and female germ cells with safety.

But it would be invidious only to regard matters from this point of view. We must go to the other extreme and see what the fertilized ovum accomplishes. It has a twofold task.

First it must bring about the wonderful organization of the mature body through a long chain of successive reactions from the simplest beginnings. Secondly, it must faithfully guard the inheritance mass entrusted to it. These two things, the performance of the ovum and that of the mature body, are the two poles of life upon which rest the harmony of our being. But this harmony is not always vouchsafed us. In vertebrates which are organized for a long life it is present to a high degree, but in some insects in which a protracted period, often a year, of quiescent larval life is followed by an adult life which can be reckoned in days only and which has but one object, to bring about the union of the sexes; the harmony is disturbed, since one phase has quite overshadowed the other. The other extreme is found in Man. He has broken through the limitations of Nature and has gone his own way. In him the individual life has grown to such a mighty tree that it has acquired an independent value, of the same importance as that of the germ cells. Marriage which remains childless because no children are desired is the opposite to the mayflies in which the importance of individual life has shrunk almost to nothing. The former, as is understandable, does not occur among animals.

4

THE DIFFERENCE BETWEEN THE SEXES (SEXUAL DIMORPHISM)

AMONG the lowest animals where in sexual matters no division of labour has occurred, males and females usually look the same. The male sea-urchin resembles the female so exactly that even the naturalist has the greatest difficulty in distinguishing between them. The male jelly-fish looks exactly like the female. But in worms it is already possible in some cases to find differences between the sexes, and in the more highly organized animals, the arthropods and vertebrates, the difference between the two is so great that one can be easily misled into placing the male into one species and the female into a different species, even into different genera or families, until field observations convince us that they belong together.

This sexual dimorphism, as it is called, can be illustrated by two examples, beginning with ourselves. With present-day fashions it becomes somewhat difficult to know whether one is looking at a young girl in trousers or an effeminate youth; but in a state of Nature the man, with his spreading beard, which in itself forms a manly decoration and which we only cut off through the idiocy of fashion, and with his deep voice, is as far apart as the poles from the more delicate beauty of the woman. The difference between the lion and the lioness is equally evident, as is that of the stag and the hind, the peacock and the peahen, and so on. In other instances the differences are less marked yet are still quite distinct. A bull, for instance, has neither mane nor beard but is unmistakable by his whole build, by the powerful neck, the straight back and many other characteristics. Only in a few cases is the difference between the sexes difficult or impossible to see. This applies to hyenas, in which male and female cannot be distinguished even by veterinary surgeons.

(a) SECONDARY SEXUAL CHARACTERS

In an attempt to find out whence these differences actually arise, science has arrived at a remarkable solution. Many of these characteristics do not develop if the animals are castrated in their youth. The castrated lion does not grow a mane, still less does a sacred baboon; the eunuch grows no beard and the stag no real antlers. We call these characteristics, which evidently depend on the reproductive glands, or rather on the sex hormones contained in them, secondary sexual characters. The conditions are, however, rather involved. If for instance one castrates a young drake or cock pheasant, the bird does not change at all in outward appearance and wears its resplendently coloured dress as before. One might think that in precisely these birds, which in their radiant colouring and the splendour of their plumage appear to us as the prototype of male beauty, everything would depend on the sex hormones, but we find that this is not so.

The answer is found only when we carry out a similar operation on the female bird, which is generally so drab in her brown dress. Now we get a surprise. The previously modest ducks or hen pheasants now carry the male dress in its full glory. The duck even grows the two odd little drake's feathers on the tail, which seem to us to be the special male attributes, and the hen pheasant grows the long tail as well as the bright colours. How are we to explain this? The females also have the sex hormones in their blood, and it is they obviously that transform the splendid male attire, which has nothing to do with sexuality, into the unobtrusive protective female dress.

Thus the sex hormones play a part in this interesting phenomenon, even though it is different to the one we had previously presumed. But there are other sex differences which have nothing to do with them. In this respect the insects are particularly remarkable, for, according to experience so far, castration affects nothing, not even in their general behaviour. The castrated male butterfly shows an equally tempestuous desire for the female as does a normal one.

The sex hormones give us some idea of the manner in which sexual differences come into being during the development of the individual, but we would also like to know how they originated. It is also note-worthy that it is precisely the highest groups of animals, in the insects and the vertebrates, that the most outstanding differences between male and female occur. Nature is therefore obviously trying to widen the gap farther and farther between male and female. Darwin in a famous paper advanced a doctrine of the sexual selection in breeding which runs somewhat like this: in mating a choice is not always but is frequently possible. Let us select an example of free choice: from her numerous suitors, the female bird can perhaps choose the one which sings most beautifully or presents the most gorgeous appearance. The female fur seal perhaps chooses the biggest and strongest amongst all the bulls present. Such choice through a constantly similar tendency in taste on the part of the females doing the choosing, a taste which persists and repeats itself through hundreds of years, can gradually transform the sex being chosen in the desired direction. This is only an hypothesis, which cannot be proved and yet which is not improbable. To this we must add a very pertinent question. Who in fact *does* choose, and who is chosen? In the following pages the reader will doubtless be convinced that in this dimorphism the male sex almost always has the advantage. Nature has lent him numerous special attributes, whilst the females modestly retire into the background. This, however, indicates that in mating, at least, the ladies' choice frequently prevails and we shall see that the behaviour of the beasts confirms this.

In what follows we shall examine matters in greater detail and see by what special characteristics the sexes are distinguished from each other.

(b) SIZE

It is simpler to commence with that group of animals to which man, in a zoological sense, belongs, namely the mammals. Here we find an almost universal rule: the male is larger and stronger than the female. We will see later that this important fact exerts a great influence on the behaviour of the sexes. In mammals the female must very often sub-ordinate her desires to those of the stronger male. Incidentally, there seems to be here a certain relation to the form of family life. The most pronounced differences in size occur amongst those species which have a true harem economy, so that one male lords it over many females. In fur seals, for example, the males are enormous, with a weight comparable with that of a horse; the females are delicate creatures weighing little more than a hundredweight. In sacred baboons, which also are the happy possessors of a harem, the differences are not so great, but here also the male is at least twice the size of the female (see Plate II). The rest of the mammals need not be mentioned in detail. We all know the proportionate sizes among domestic animals, such as cattle, sheep and pigs and also those among some wild beasts. The sole exceptions are, oddly enough, among the giants of the animal kingdom, the whalebone whales. In these, the females are a little the larger, and thus the privilege that the largest beasts existing upon earth belong to their sex is with the ladies.

In the remaining vertebrates, size does not play such an important part, and we will pass over them somewhat more briefly. In birds we find both, that is, those in which the male is the larger and those in which the female is the larger; in either case there is the same dependence on the marital conditions. Amongst birds there are no harems, but there are those species in which the males are promiscuous and others which practise the strictest monogamy. Among the former, to which many fowls belong, the bustards, birds of paradise and others, the male is always considerably larger, and here there is no doubt whatever that it is a true ladies' choice in mating. In monogamy, conditions are equalized and we know of numerous examples where the females are the more majestic. In birds of prey this seems generally to be the case; the female sparrow-hawk is double the size of the male.

In reptiles the males are, for the most part, the larger. In amphibians, on the other hand, the opposite is true. It is a matter of common observation that the female toad or frog is much larger than the male. In many species like the African clawed toad the difference is immense. It can hardly be assumed that the choice of a mate played a part in the development of these differences. On the other hand, the tasks which face the two sexes during their sexual life are significant. The domestic hen, during a long life, lays its eggs at the steady rate of not more than one a day. For the production of only one egg there is no need for a large space and there is therefore no reason why the hen need be larger than the cock. On the other hand, toads and frogs when spawning lay many hundreds of eggs at a time, and if one takes hold of a female frog full of eggs in the laboratory it is possible to feel that the entire abdominal cavity is filled by the enormously swollen ovary and oviducts. For these a considerable space is necessary, and we can thus understand why the female toad needs to exceed her mate in size.

This consideration is also readily applied in the realm of the invertebrates. In spiders and in many insects the excessive size of the female, often very considerable, may be explained by the immense number of eggs that she has to drag around with her. In some spiders this has gone so far that the females may be a thousand times the weight of the male, who seems truly like a dwarf beside his gigantic mate. It is natural that here also the enormous difference in size has an important bearing on the behaviour during mating (Fig. 6).

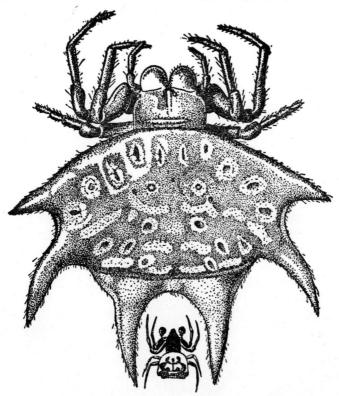

FIG. 6. Spider, *Gasteracantha curvispina*; (*above*) female, (*below*) male.

Insects do not show the same great disparity in size that we find in spiders, yet even in them we frequently find the female two to three times the size of the male. This applies especially to the full-bodied moths, represented in the European fauna by the gipsy moth, oak-egger moth and many others. The causes of this are the same as for spiders. On the other hand there are many insects in which precisely the opposite is true, the males towering above the females in size. The stag-beetle is a good example, and among the tropical beetles there are many others. So far, there is no explanation for this (see also Plate I).

(c) COLOURING

Anyone who at any time has carefully examined a collection of birds or butterflies will have been struck by the contrasting colouring shown by the sexes in the various species. The males are often of ravishing beauty. We need only recall the splendid peacock with the thousand eyes carried on his tail feathers and the wonderful blue of his neck, or of the golden pheasant with the gleaming golden yellow of his head-dress and the fiery red of his breast. The little humming-birds twinkle in all colours and glitter in the sun like jewels, and the birds of paradise are of such incomparably magic beauty that they are the gems of such a collection. The females, on the contrary, of all these birds are veritable Cinderellas. Their dress is an inconspicuous brown or grey and none of them shows what rich relations she has. In the butterflies a similar picture is presented. There is the wonderful lustre of the male lycænid and copperwing butterflies, the females of which wear drab and quite undistinguished apparel. In the purple emperor, only the males have wings radiant with a lovely violet, while the females are quite simply brown.

It is certainly no coincidence that it is in just these two groups of animals, the birds and butterflies, that the courtship display is so wide-spread. The male which pleads for favour for the sake of posterity, therefore, makes himself as lovely as possible, and Nature has spared no pains to help him. Of course, all that has been said so far is only imaginary, and at the moment there are few proofs of its truth. Something of this we will learn later. Here, however, we can attempt a proof by an indirect method, in at least one case. Male humming-birds scintillate in all colours. Head, breast, back and tail are of an indescrib-ably splendid colouring; the wings are by contrast a simple brown or grey. What this means can be understood when one sees these little creatures in flight. In contrast to the other birds which move their wings quite slowly, the humming-birds belong to the "buzz" flyers and move their wings with a rapid vibration resembling that of the hawk-moths. The wings vibrate sixty to seventy times a second, so rapidly that their

PLATE V.
Billing doves.

Male green lizard, "dominant" in front of his own reflection in a mirror.

PLATE VI.
Amherst pheasant, "displaying" whilst strutting in front of a female.

Roman or edible snail. Preliminary to mating.

beat cannot be followed by any eye. A pretty colour on the wings would thus serve no purpose for showing off, and that it is absent in spite of the magnificence of the rest of the plumage is a clear proof that the variegated colours of the rest are there to be admired. They await a beholder whose heart to ravish.

There is another reason, however, why the females are so inconspicuously clad. The clothing is protective. The hen pheasant, which nests on the ground and must continue to sit when a fox is stalking, must not blaze in vivid colours. She must match the ground and must be adapted to it so that the contours of her body will merge into the dry grass and the leaves and twigs which lie round her. Now we begin to understand the reason why in birds the female sex hormone converts the full dress into a protective cover. A high wisdom manifests itself in these things, and in Nature the inconspicuous plumage does not denote taking a back seat.

The same considerations apply to butterflies. When the male has completed his mating his earthly task is done—"The Moor has his duty done, the Moor may go". Nature is never concerned with the individual, only with provision, and to a much higher degree, for the race. For this the fertilized female is of the greatest importance, for she has the duty of laying the tiny eggs on the natural food plant of the caterpillar. During this activity a too conspicuous apparel would not be a good thing.

(d) NUPTIAL DRESS

In a whole series of animals, the two sexes may be alike for the rest of the year but at mating time the males decorate themselves with all sorts of pretty colours. This we call a nuptial dress, and it is found in many fish, amphibians and reptiles. Whether we are justified in adding to these the full dress of many male birds, the pheasant perhaps or the peacock, is a matter of taste, since this dress persists throughout the year. But one can certainly count the beautiful colouring of some male butterflies as a nuptial robe, for the short life of these creatures is devoted almost exclusively to love.

This nuptial dress or wedding garment hides many secrets. Plain common sense certainly tells me that it must be present to react upon the female and to make her ready for love. But other hypotheses have also been put forward. Some naturalists believe that these beauties only appeal to our eyes, and that the glad rags are the involuntary reaction to a heightened vital force which fills the male animal at the mating season. We will therefore try to show whether or not the marriage garb is of any use (see also the chapter on courtship display).

There is much to be said for the view that the wedding garment is there to be seen. In fish only those males wear gay colours whose females spawn in daylight and in shallow water. All species which spawn in dark deeps or at night preserve their inconspicuous colour even during mating time. This is a clear indication which can hardly mean anything else but that the gay dress is there to be seen by the female.

In fish particularly Nature has used all her arts to achieve the most drastic effects possible. Let us begin with the stickleback. The spawnless male wears a fairly inconspicuous covering. On a paler grey ground there are some darker stripes and greenish markings, and that is all. In the courting male, however, the belly and flanks become a fiery red, the back a delicate pale green, the iris of the eyes azure. This gay dress is caused by the redistribution of the chromatophores, and also by the enlargement of the blood capillaries of the skin. It is dependent on the sex hormones, but physical circumstances also have a strong influence. During a fight between the males the victor always remains much more beautifully coloured than the vanquished, who rapidly loses his fiery hues; he becomes pale and soon after his defeat he appears not very different to the spawnless sticklebacks.

The mighty salmon also can assume a wedding garment of fine colours. The belly becomes purple-red, and red patches which merge in zigzag stripes adorn the head. These red marks show particularly well against the bluish background of the rest of the skin.

The wedding dress of certain tropical toothed carps is perhaps the most beautifully developed, and these are kept nowadays by many amateurs as ornamental fish. In the genus *Aphyosemion* each species appears more beautiful than the last, and it is really difficult to decide which of them deserves the prize. The extraordinary effect of the nuptial dress may well reside in every case on the contrasting colours. In *A. arnoldi* the ground colour of the body is blue-green at the head and at the root of the tail a deep indigo blue. The whole body is patterned with small red spots which run together into stripes in the forward half of the body. The fins also are characterized by equally contrasting colours. Red predominates at the base of the fin which passes into yellow-green, and along the edge runs a dark stripe, while the fins are also everywhere decorated with small red patches. No artist's imagination could have produced a more enchanting creation.

In newts the coloration is perhaps less striking than in fish, but there the nuptial dress is distinguished by certain morphological characteristics. The crested newt (*Triton cristatus*) grows an enormous dorsal comb in the spring which runs from the head to the root of the tail and is marked by a number of serrations. The region around the cloaca becomes swollen. Of the colours the quarter inch wide mother-of-pearl or silvery streak running the length of the tail is the most remarkable. The belly is a vivid orange marked with numerous large spots, and on the throat there is a great quantity of white dots in addition to these spots.

In the common newt (*Triton vulgaris*) the difference between the normal inconspicuous colouring and the nuptial dress is so great that originally individuals wearing it were believed to represent different species. The skin in the common newt is sprinkled with small white dots, the ground colour being a rich olive green which merges into white towards the belly, and on the head is interrupted by blackish longitudinal bands. On the trunk it is ornamented with numerous black spots. These spots are usually arranged in longitudinal rows on the body and tail. About the middle of the belly the pale yellow is replaced by a bright orange. Besides all this the beast has a bluish or mother-of-pearl longitudinal stripe.

The most beautiful of all newts seems to be the *Triturus vittatus ophryticus* Gray, from Asia Minor. Plate I, although not coloured, gives a rough idea of it.

(e) SENSE ORGANS

Whilst size seems to be connected with the problem of sexual selection and the colouring of the male with courtship display, a consideration of the various developments of the sense organs in males and females leads to a further biological problem, namely the search for the opposite sex. As we shall see in greater detail later, that is a task falling almost exclusively to the male, and since for this sharp senses are necessary it is not surprising that the males occasionally possess the better-developed sense organs. Much more remarkable is the fact that differences in the sense organs should be restricted to a single group of animals, namely the insects, which in this respect are outstanding. At most there may also be some bristle-worms which show these marked differences, which are wholly absent in the vertebrates.

The sense of smell is the one most affected. For instance, there is the marine bristle-worm, in which there are two generations, one which creeps about the sea-bed and a second which swims free in the sea, and hence belongs to the so-called pelagic animals. In this second generation the males are furnished with immensely large tentacles or feelers, with which evidently they find the females. The same can be said of the

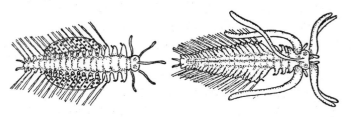

FIG. 7. Chætopod, *Autolytus varians*; (*left*) female, (*right*) male.

crustacea. The males of these have well-developed first antennæ, which are generally regarded as their organs of smell, while those of the females are only poorly developed.

Amongst our native insects this marked difference is particularly striking in some moths, especially the spinners. The males of these have very long feathered antennæ, with innumerable sensory cells on each of their side branches. The females have only short comb-like antennæ. Here a very neat relation can be seen between the flying abilities of the females and the development of the antennæ in the males. In those species in which both sexes fly well, the difference in the structure of the antennæ is quite small. The less able the females are to fly, the more the male has to exert himself to find a female and the greater is the development of his antennæ. Finally in species in which the females have lost their wings entirely, the male antennæ are the most strongly developed.

A great rarity, oddly enough, is the better development of the eyes in males. There are only a few examples amongst the flies and the may-flies, which are, however, not true flies. Naturally this is connected with the fact that in these instances the female is sought with the help of the eyes.

(f) WINGS

There are many insects in which the females have lost their wings, while the males remain in full possession of them. Fundamentally, this seems very peculiar, since the flying insects have a great advantage over nearly all other creatures, namely that their broods can be distributed wholly by the female flying here and there and laying her eggs over a wide area. This advantage has been forgone by the wingless ones. In practice, however, it can be seen that this suits them very well, for many among them, like the hybernia geometrid, have become a pest in spite of the limitation. Of course, seeking out the opposite sex for the purpose of mating has become in these cases an exclusively male duty. This phenomenon is most frequent in the moths, especially the geometrids. There are, however, also wingless owl-moth females. The degree of degeneration in the wings is exceedingly variable. They may be only slightly reduced in size, they may be reduced to tiny stumps or they may have disappeared completely.

There are, however, also amongst the other groups of insects some which are similarly placed. Examples are the weevils, the cockroaches, the leaf insects or phasmides, and, amongst the hymenoptera, the mutillids.

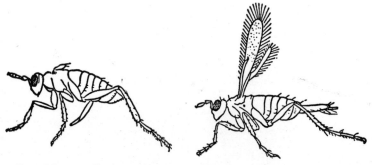

FIG. 8. Ichneumon fly, *Prestwichia aquatica*; (*left*) wingless male, (*right*) winged female.

The reverse, in which the males are wingless and the females have preserved their wings, is much more rare and is always connected with very special biological conditions. The first example is the aquatic ichneumon fly, *Prestwichia aquatica*. Both sexes normally live in water, where pairing may also take place. The female lays her eggs in the eggs of other aquatic insects. Therefore she needs wings to give her a greater radius of action. In some perlides (*Tarniopteryx trifasciata*) the egg laying takes place whilst the female hovers close to the surface of the water and drops the eggs in small clumps. For this purpose the wings are essential. The remainder of her life is spent entirely close to the water's edge, where she may be seen running about on stones or plants. The males of this species therefore have no need of wings.

Finally a particularly remarkable instance of a wingless male insect is provided by the fig insects (*Blastophaga grossorum*), also belonging to the hymenoptera. The eggs here are laid in wild figs, inside the male fruit buds, and develop into galls. The males never leave the region of these galls. Each opens his own gall by means of powerful mandibles and eats his way into another gall occupied by a female. There mating takes place at once and the life of the male is ended. To the females remains the task of distributing the eggs among the buds of other fig trees, and for this they need wings.

(g) CLIMBING AND CLASPING ORGANS

Many of the lower animals have yet another peculiarity which must be included under sexual dimorphism. The males are frequently equipped with clasping organs enabling them to clasp the body of the

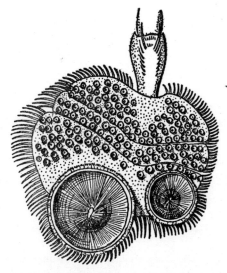

FIG. 9. Disc at the tip of the foreleg of the male margined water-beetle, *Dytiscus marginalis*, with sucking cups (suckers) for holding fast the female.

female when mating. Claspers of this sort are found among all the lower animals, from the worms upwards. Since we are concerned here more with the way of life of animals than with their anatomy, we must be very brief on this very interesting subject. Male threadworms, to which belong roundworms and many others, have at their hinder end the so-called *bursa copulatrix*, a fold of skin in which they can enclose the body of the female. The margined water-beetle (*Dytiscus marginalis*) has on its forefeet large gripping discs each carrying two large suckers as well as a number of smaller ones. Male copepods, small agile crustaceans, found everywhere in the sea and in fresh water, have so-called grasping antennæ with which they can attach themselves firmly to the female's tail during the initial phase of mating. Finally there is an example of the same sort of thing among the vertebrates. Male frogs have the well-known thumb pad, a secondary sexual character depending on the male sex hormones. It also is of importance in clasping the female.

(h) SEXUAL WEAPONS

The difference between the sexes is also marked by the so-called sexual weapons, which in a fight with his rivals are often of vital importance to the male. Here we can only consider a few examples. Among our cousins the apes, the males have terrifying eye-teeth. In a zoo one may see a male baboon opening his mouth to yawn. It is a fearsome sight. There are four powerful canine teeth which would not disgrace a beast of prey. They are quite as long as those of a leopard, and even more dangerous, for they have a sharp edge on the inner side by which means the wound is enlarged. These beasts are, however, by no means carnivorous. They eat fruit and other delicate parts of plants; they do occasionally take and eat a grasshopper or a fat caterpillar, but never anything bigger. The canines can serve them only to fight their sexual battles, which will be discussed later. With them and their powerful claws they defend their harems.

Another beast in which the males carry enormous canine teeth is the wild pig. Known as tusks, they are much weaker in the females. The antlers of stags also belong to the category of sexual weapons, as do the antlers of reindeer and many others.

Through numerous transitions these weapons are connected with the so-called decorative organs in the male animals, and especially in insects. The somewhat bizarre growths which can be seen on the heads and backs of many beetles, such as the lamellicorns, can hardly be of importance in every case as weapons. We just have to be content to admire them without being able to ascribe a function to them.

(i) DWARF MALES

In the final part of this chapter we must again return to the problem of size. In a whole series of lower animals, among the worms and crustacea, are to be found the so-called dwarf males. One might imagine that a male spider, which is a thousand times smaller than his mate, could after all be fully entitled to be regarded as a dwarf male. There is, however, an important difference here. The male spider is a fully constructed small spider, who is quite independent throughout his life. He spins his web, catches his prey and feeds himself entirely. Only in his very small size is he in any way exceptional. The true dwarf males, on the other hand, may best be described as stunted rudiments. They have lost a great part of their organization; in most cases they have for instance absolutely no intestinal tract. Nearly their whole interior is filled by a huge seed-pod, to which is attached an ejecting apparatus. They are in fact actually only small transport machines for the seed contained in their interior. We can express this as follows: Nature has left only that part of the individuality of the male which is directly necessary for propagation and the preservation of the species; every other individual feature has vanished.

Let us have a closer look at a series of these remarkable beings. If you happen to be bathing in the lovely blue Adriatic on a rocky shore and turn over some stones lying in the shallows, it may be that you will capture a very rare worm. Its blue-green body has roughly the size and shape of a plum, but runs into an extraordinarily long proboscis in front, which can be over eighteen inches long and ends in two transverse lobes. This worm, called *Bonellia viridis* (Fig. 10), gave the first naturalist to find it many a headache; for all the specimens found were females. There seemed to be no males at all. By more careful examination it was then discovered that in the outer genital passage there usually existed a number of tiny glittering creatures, which, regarded superficially, might well have been taken to be relatives of the well-known slipper animalcule (*Paramœcium*). Under the microscope, however, it could be seen that they were, without a shadow of doubt, multicellular animals. Moreover, one could see, in their interior, an organ that was certainly a male seminal gland. The riddle had been solved; the tiny beasts were the dwarf males of the giant worm. When the eggs were hatched out they brought confirmation and at the same time disclosed a new, very rare fact. If the eggs are hatched in a glass bowl of clean sea-water then they will all develop into females. If males are needed, an artifice must be adopted; one must place a small piece of the female proboscis in the bowl. This piece of proboscis, for which an extract from a proboscis may be substituted, has a magic influence on all the eggs so that they develop into males. We cannot pursue this interesting problem any further here, but it contains, even to this day, many unanswered questions. We will now look round us for further dwarf males.

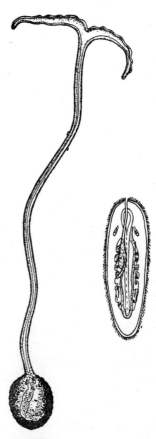

Anyone going to sea in a North Sea trawler will notice that, in addition to the numerous fish, the catch will include many whelks. A number of these may be empty, that is, the whelk that built the shell has long been dead, but inside the shell there may be a peculiar guest, namely a hermit-crab. If we break up one of these inhabited shells with care and take careful note of the fragments, then we shall see in the outer convolutions of the shell a number of small black lines. If we make a small excavation at this spot we shall see that the hermit-crab was not the only inhabitant of this house but that he also had a number of sub-tenants.

Fig. 10. Marine worm, *Bonellia viridis*; (*left*) female, (*right*) male (latter greatly magnified).

Each of these sub-tenants, as we have called them, is in fact another kind of crustacean related to the barnacles. Named *Alcippe lampas*, it is two to three tenths of an inch long and as shapeless as a sack. Its interior is almost entirely filled by eggs, and as with *Bonellia* we have here nothing but females. Profiting by our acquaintance with the dwarf male of that worm, we start to search for similar creatures, and our industry is soon rewarded. We find on the outer skin of the female, near the genital opening, some very remarkable structures. There may be only two of them, but there may be five or even a round dozen. No one would take these for crustaceans. They have the shape of a pistol. In the part corresponding to the grip is a huge testicle visible through the translucent skin. The barrel is filled by an ejaculatory apparatus which forces the sperms into the genital passage of the giant female. That we have not been deceived is proved also by the history of the development in this species. Minute larvæ, the so-called nauplii, are hatched from the numerous eggs produced by this crustacean, and these swim freely by means of their six legs. At this stage, it is not possible to say which will turn out to be male and which female. Moreover, we have no means of changing the sex. Probably the little creatures know each other at an early age by instinct, for while the female larvæ after a short free-swimming period enter a shell occupied by a hermit, the males seek out the small cracks in the shell through which the females have worked their way inside and there they complete their development.

Bonellia and *Alcippe* are isolated cases, but in rotifers, microscopic worm-like inhabitants of fresh water, there are on the contrary many species which have these dwarf males. Generally we can distinguish three groups in this extensive order of animals. The seisonids behave normally throughout, males and females being about the same size; bdelloids have got rid of their males entirely, of which more will be said later; and all the families between these two extremes have dwarf males. They are not so degenerate as those we have so far discussed. Above all they can swim about very actively, but they have no intestine and their life is therefore strictly limited and directed to one and only one object.

Formerly, it was generally assumed that the somewhat despicable treatment Nature had meted out to the male sex, of having to suffer the indignity of the creation of dwarf males, was confined to the lower animals. There was justifiable astonishment therefore when a fish with dwarf males was also found. Here we are dealing with a rare monster of the deep (Fig. 11), which only a few naturalists have seen alive, and the discovery of the dwarf males was not made in the wide open spaces but in a museum. The female of this fish is of a respectable size, over eighteen inches in length. In the course of a detailed examination of the female it was found that at the sides of the abdomen there were some unexplained excrescences which were at first assumed to be normal parts of the fish's body and which were firmly attached to her. Only later was it realized that here we had an especially peculiar sort of dwarf

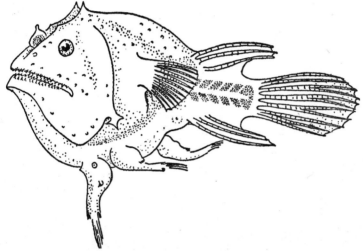

FIG. 11. Deep-sea fish, *Edriolychnus schmidti*. Three dwarf males securely grown on to the abdominal surface of the large female.

male. Even now nothing further is known about it. Nevertheless, it is probable that the males first grip the female's skin with their teeth and finally merge with her. Certainly this is the best way to solve the food problem, for the dwarf males must obviously be connected to the blood system of the big female, so that they need not bother about either food or breath.

(k) ATROPHY IN THE FEMALE

It is of interest to inquire whether there ever occur females comparable to the dwarf males. It is not in this sense a matter of size, and dwarf females are found nowhere in the world. The decisive point is whether there exist females in which the bodily organization is so reduced that in the end only the sexual organs remain, that is to say, organs for the production of eggs in this case.

In fact several instances of this may be listed. In the termites the sexes look exactly the same at first. When, however, mating is concluded the queen sheds her wings, builds a living-chamber and starts to lay eggs. Then the rear part of her body swells in a truly incredible manner, so that the males, which were originally equal in size to the queen, now seem like dwarfs beside her (Fig. 12). But the now fully grown female has become purely an egg-laying machine. In the more primitive termites this is not quite so strongly marked. The queen in *Nasutermes surinamensis* is one inch long and lays 2,938 eggs in twenty-four hours. That of *Anoplotermes silvestri* reaches a size of two inches and a production of 7,568 eggs per day. But these all fade into insignificance beside the queen of *Bellicositermes natalensis*, which is a giantess of four inches and which will lay 36,000 eggs in the course of a day. If we work this out we find it amounts to 1,500 an hour, twenty-five every minute or roughly an egg every other second. This creature really has become a pure egg-laying machine, whose production would turn many a factory owner green with envy. But the individual life has been destroyed from the foundation up. Round the queen there are dozens of workers. The giant being, which is now quite immobile, is fed in front, at the rear her excrement is removed and the eggs which have been laid are moved away. Along her sides many workers are busy with cleaning this gross body. Here then we have the equivalent of the dwarf males.

To a lesser degree the wingless females of some moths may be called egg-laying machines. The whole life of the female vapourer moth (*Orgyia antiqua*) is passed as follows. As soon as the plump, sluggish creature has freed herself from the wrappings of the pupa and has crept out of the cocoon she seats herself upon the latter. The winged males arrive without delay, mating is consummated and the concluding stages of the life of the female moth proceed precisely as for the termite queen, with the laying of eggs. When that ends, as it does in a few days, then life also is finished. We may say of this, that by human standards it is not easy to judge whether it was worth it or not.

(*l*) THE ABOLITION OF THE MALE
Parthenogenesis

In their stunted condition the dwarf males have already lost much of the appearance associated with their sex. But what provides more food for thought is the fact that in a large number of animals the males have

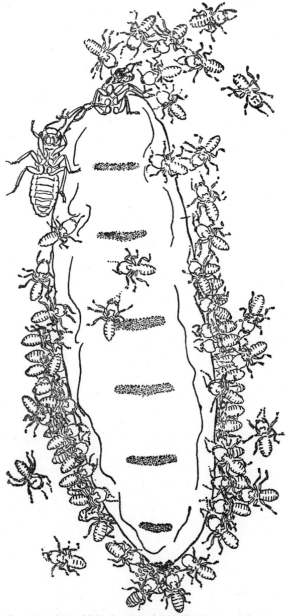

FIG. 12. A glance into the wedding chamber of the *Bellicositermes natalensis*, termites, seen from below. Many workers are seen round the large queen; at her fore-end, left, a male.

partly or wholly disappeared. We find this abnormality in a number of worms, and also in crustacea and insects. The vertebrates have managed to avoid this degradation of the male sex.

We must, however, go to the very heart of this problem. We have seen that the most profound expression of the whole sexual process lies in the ovum being fertilized by the sperm. When there are no longer any males then fertilization is no longer possible, and the ova must call upon some mysterious ability to develop without fertilization. How this is possible we do not yet know.

The case which has been known for the longest time is that of the honey bee, and the story of the discovery of *parthenogenesis* or *virgin birth* is so remarkable that it is worth looking into a little more closely. The bee-keeper knew ages ago that so-called drone-broody queens existed, from whose eggs only drones, but no worker bees or queens, could hatch. Such creatures are naturally useless, but nobody could explain the phenomenon. A simple Silesian village priest, named Dzierzon, noticed, roughly a hundred years ago, that this drone-broodiness occurred in two different kinds of queens: in quite old queens and in those with crippled wings, so that the mating flight, without which mating cannot take place, could not be carried out by them. It needed, by any standards, considerable perspicacity to draw the conclusion from these two findings, that the drone-broodiness bears some relation to the state of the stock of sperms in the queen. It could be presumed that the supply of sperms which the old queen had acquired during the mating flight gradually diminished, while the young one which had had no nuptial flight never had carried any. This hypothesis was capable of proof, for even at that time it was known that the fertilized queen carried with her the sperms, which, astonishingly, remain alive for over three years, in a small spherical container, the *receptaculum seminis*. Dzierzon, who possessed neither a microscope nor a magnifying glass but only a keen intellect and a sharp eye, now made the following experiment. He removed the entire genital tract from a normal queen and observed, by holding the organ against the light of a window, that the little seed-bladder was filled with a milky liquid. When the experiment was repeated with a drone-broody queen he always found that the little bladder was as clear as water. From this he concluded with absolute certainty that the eggs from which the drones originated were unfertilized. Thus he was able to prove the occurrence of parthenogenesis in the animal kingdom. Science could but admit that nothing remained to be added to the discoveries of this man, who was not a professional, but a born, naturalist.

Although in bees parthenogenesis is linked with another difficult problem, that of sex determination, in most other animals it fulfils the task of ensuring as rapid an increase of the species as possible during a favourable season. This happens in the water-flea, a small lively crustacean found in ponds in reddish swarms in summer. In summer there are only females and not a single male water-flea. Each female carries in her brood pouch a number of offspring which doubtless are nourished by the mother and which again are all females. Let us assume that each mother brings only six young into the world. This makes seven families capable of producing in the next generation forty-two progeny. Including grandmother and mothers we already have fifty, so that we must be prepared soon for 300 great-grandchildren. We now have at our disposal 358 ripe females, and before long these will increase to thousands. It is obvious that this process would take longer if the eggs had to be fertilized. Then there would be only half as many females; the others would be males. If we commence with one pair of parents there would be, in the same generation, only four females, including the mother, with twenty-four young. We would then have sixteen females, while with parthenogenesis fifty would be ready for further increases. We need not take our arithmetic any farther to show that the males would be a hindrance if the greatest and most rapid possible increase is the desired end. In autumn, of course, the picture alters, for then, quite suddenly, male water-fleas also are hatched. From the union between these and the females available at the time so-called winter eggs are produced, from which, when spring returns, a new generation of parthenogenetic females emerges.

To say the least, bees and water-fleas cannot mislead the male sex into the highfalutin belief that the world cannot carry on without them. The next group of animals we examine frees us further from this foolish superstition. There are certain species in which naturalists have seen not a single male during the three centuries since the discovery of the microscope, and in which, even with the most careful breeding experiments, none has ever been discovered. It follows from this that in these species there can be no males at all, and that the male sex is quite redundant. This is true of a family of rotifers, the so-called Bdelloidea, and also of a large number of free-living threadworms and of some crustacea. It is true that their number is small compared to the vast mass of the other species, yet by their very existence they have provided a very important proof.

It is possible then to imagine a world in which there are no men. We do not need to argue whether it would be more perfect than the one we are compelled to live in, but we hope to be able to prove that it could well be a more boring one.

In some species the occurrence of parthenogenesis depends on circumstances. The Indian stick insect (*Dixippus morosus*) lives quite normally in India, its native country, for there there are as many males as females. In European countries, where it is bred in nearly every laboratory, no males whatever appear and the entire sexual activities of these despisers of men are confined to laying an egg and dropping it to the ground.

In certain of our native species of crustacea known as *Apus* and *Triops* much the same thing may be found. In Germany only female specimens have been found; in Spain, on the other hand, there are numerous males as well. Goethe, who with his universal genius also gave some attention to this corner of nature-study, offered a solid dollar as a prize to anyone who would bring him a male *Apus;* he could not get rid of his dollar. Goethe was probably interested in these things because parthenogenesis was at that time being discussed but dismissed by the leading naturalists with the dictum: *Ex nihilo nihil fit* (From nothing, nothing).

5

ATTRACTION OF THE OPPOSITE SEX

THE most important prerequisite for mating is that the sexes should meet. This is naturally not difficult amongst beasts which live in larger or smaller groups. On the whole, however, this is exceptional. The great majority of animals live solitary lives, and the mating season is the only time when the trails of two individuals meet for a brief space. In these cases special provision is made so that at the appropriate time a meeting really does take place.

It may be taken as an axiom here, as usual in the biology of sex, that the male is the active partner. Even so, two very different methods may be noted. In the first, the male actually seeks out the female, who stays put; in the second, the male entices the female to him. Both are brought about naturally by means of certain sensory impressions which in the first instance must affect the male and in the second the female. There is, however, a highly peculiar contrast. In by far the greater number the males are guided to the female by scent. On the other hand, the enticement of the female is never brought about, as far as we know at present, by those means. On the contrary it is hearing which plays the most important part, assisted by sight.

We will examine a few instances in a little more detail.

(a) THE SEARCH FOR THE FEMALES BY THE MALES

As one example let us choose the insects, where behaviour is particularly clear and impressive. The biology of sex in insects differs markedly and in a variety of ways from that of most other animals. Vertebrates attain sexual maturity gradually. In insects, on the contrary, the life-history is divided as with a sharp knife into three different phases: the larval life, the pupa and the imago. These three stages are completely different, not only in appearance but also in importance. The larva's only responsibility is that its body measurements shall reach the necessary dimensions: its sole task is feeding, feeding and more feeding. The life of the imago on the other hand has but one significance, namely the need for propagation. In it nourishment is a secondary consideration. Where feeding does occur, as in cockchafers and female gnats, its only purpose is to secure the full development of the sexual organs. In very many other instances its only importance is to keep life's motor ticking over. In many species, for instance in the spinners, no food at all is taken during this last period of life. The males of these species, as soon as they have left the shelter of the chrysalis and are able to fly, have but one impulse, namely to seek out a female and mate with her. What goes on in the tiny brain meanwhile remains a complete mystery and all the efforts of science to discover it have been in vain. Only one thing we can see, and that is that the male spinner quickly begins a tempestuous and restless search in a flight which lasts for the whole of his very short life and probably suffers no interruption save in the hours of rest of the daily rhythm.

We can get a very realistic picture of these things in spring, when the apple blossom is out. In Europe as the buds are bursting in a beechwood a large rusty red moth may be seen flying erratically and swiftly just above the ground, up and down without ever resting. This is the male of the tau (*Aglia tau*) in his unceasing search for a mate. The much larger females sit the whole day long with spread wings at the foot of a beech trunk, there to await events.

These flights into the blue, so to speak, arise from an inner urge, without any special stimulus from outside acting on the creatures. In the course of these reconnoitring flights it happens that the moth passes purely by accident near a female and becomes aware of the delicate perfume emanating from her. At this stage they soon find one another.

Although the whole affair can be described in a few simple words, the account of some first-hand observations is not without its surprises. The first to occupy himself with this rare problem was the Swiss entomologist Forel. He kept newly hatched female moths (probably small hawk-moths) in a wire cage on his balcony in the centre of the town, and observed the nightly arrival of numerous males, although their normal habitat was actually far away. Since it seemed incomprehensible to a sane human mind that a distant scenting of the fragrance could occur over a distance of several miles, the belief was soon held that the female moth did not in fact exude scent but emitted rays of some kind. Forel, however, had the lucky idea of proving this hypothesis by the following experiment. Instead of a female he set out on the balcony a piece of paper on which a fresh female had sat for several hours. He found that the males flew to this paper also. With this simple experiment the ray hypothesis was exploded and the scent hypothesis re-established.

Very interesting experiments were also made a generation ago by a German naturalist, Mell, in South China. Although they produced nothing new scientifically, the method used again proved the astonishing ability of the male spinners to "wind" the females. He used large tropical silk-moths (*Actias selene*). These splendid moths, with a wing-span of four inches, can be easily marked by cutting small nicks in one of their large wings. They can then be recognized individually. Mell proceeded by having a large cage, in which the newly hatched females had room to fly, built on his veranda. A friend of his went inland by train with a number of marked males and at every station he released a few of them. Mell could then tell what proportion of these males returned to his veranda. The result was quite startling. Of twenty males released eight (40 per cent) returned from a distance of two and a half miles, and 25 per cent from a distance of seven miles.

The fact itself, then, is not in doubt. What answer do we make if, in spite of this, the hypothesis of "scenting" over a distance of several miles is denied? It is, for example, possible to imagine a male moth making a kind of reconnaissance flight. It would be very difficult to prove this, yet it could conceivably happen. Let us assume that in searching the male sets out from a given point and proceeds to circle this point in irregular rings which gradually increase in diameter. In this way the whole area around the point of departure would be systematically searched. In the course of this it could happen that the moth, by pure accident, does come near the resting place of the female, let us say to within a hundred yards. Then and only then need the "winding" or "scenting" be brought into operation.

This hypothesis could also explain the following chance observation, made many years ago in Vienna. Several collectors who lived in different parts of the town, separated by various distances, had had sent to them in chrysalis form similar tropical silk-moths to those described by

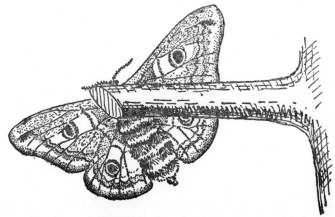

FIG. 13. Female of the small emperor moth, *Saturnia pavonia*, with forward-thrust scent organ at rear end of abdomen, awaiting the approach of the male on the wing.

Mell. One of them had a son of the right age to get into mischief. One night when his father was out he let some males escape through the window. These valuable specimens were, however, not lost, but arrived on the balcony of one of the other collectors who chanced to have some freshly hatched females there.

Of the rest of the animal world we know, unfortunately, very little as yet on this interesting subject. The behaviour of dogs is familiar and quite remarkable. A bitch on heat, no matter how secluded she may be kept, will attract dozens of dogs of all breeds, even though we humans may not notice anything at all of the emanations from the bitch.

The visual signal which serves to attract the opposite sex is shown by the well-known glow-worm. On any fine warm June night dozens of these glowing little creatures may be seen flying about in appropriate wooded spots. They are all males, all intent on finding females, which rest on the grass and there exhibit their fixed lights. Little research has been made into the biology of the sex of our native glow-worm. On the other hand, many interesting details about an American species of firefly (*Photinus pyralis*) have been described. In them the sexes give out a lovely flashing light. The flying males emit a short light signal about every six seconds; the females sitting on the grass reply with great precision by flashing their lanterns exactly two seconds after the appearance of the male flash. This reply is the signal awaited by the male, which shows him that his partner is ready for mating. By flying nearer and repeating the process he soon finds himself at the goal of his desire.

The attraction of the male by visual signals, interestingly enough, has also been described in a very lowly animal, namely a marine bristle-worm. The female of the marine polychæte (*Odontosyllis enopla*) at the mating time swims, in shallow water, in narrow circles close to the surface, and glows. This light circle is the signal for the male, lying on the bottom. He swims vertically upwards into the middle of the light circle, and in this position both empty their mature germ cells into the water.

It is certain that much more has yet to be discovered about luminescent marine animals. Many deep-sea fishes and octopods shine their light through lenses which are often multi-coloured. These light organs are situated in the most extraordinary places, and there is hardly any other biological explanation possible but that the creatures recognize each other by them at the mating season.

(b) ATTRACTION OF THE FEMALES BY THE MALES
The dances of the males

In regions which are as yet undisturbed by human settlement, especially near stagnant water, one can occasionally observe in summer a wonderful natural game. At a distance of one to two miles one may see rising near the shore of a lake, or over a low bush, peculiar pillars of smoke, which at first give the impression that small boys had lit a fire. As one gets near, it can be seen that the "smoke" consists of myriads of small insects which rise and fall in a lively flight. They fly vertically upward and presently after a short flight sink down again, whereupon the game is repeated. The accompanying illustration, a copy of an old copper engraving of the year 1812, shows us that this remarkable natural game had been observed many years ago (Fig. 14).

The phenomenon differs according to the species. Among the gnats these pillars of smoke, which can occasionally be seen in the garden,

The smoking old pentagon tower with enlarged insect (inset).

FIG. 14. The smoking tower, clouds of thousands of dancing midges (chironomids) above the roof. (Reproduction of an etching of the year 1812.)

consist of only a few thousand creatures; the columns are then usually only a few yards high, rising some sixteen to twenty feet above the ground. On the other hand the midges (chironomids) which develop in some lakes, often in incredible numbers, form immense swarms well known to the local people. Wesenberg-Lund describes such a sight in his Swedish homeland in such impressive language that we cannot do better than repeat his own words: "On summer evenings they form clouds over the great Gribwald which sometimes reach a length of four miles. The clouds offer a really fantastic appearance. From their surfaces cupolas swell up and slowly form into columns of several yards height, which wave about in the light breeze, then rise and expand like the crowns of pine trees and finally disperse to make way for other clouds. The display lasts until nightfall. The clouds of chironomids shine red-gold in the evening sun and vanish gradually after sunset in the growing dark, whilst the upper parts of the columns touched by the last rays of the sun stand out golden from the pale evening sky. The cloud carpet continues to send out new columns upwards and remains in continuous wavy movement like a sea moving in a mighty swell."

These swarms, whether they consist of midges (chironomids) or any other kind of insect, always consist of males. Only the freshly hatched males following an unerring instinct carry out this aerial dance (compare the preceding illustration). But what has this to do with reproduction, and where are the females hiding? Every now and then a larger, darker midge will fly from outside and in a straight line right into the swarm of dancing males; this is a female. It seems as if she were attracted by a magic force, but whether it is a question of sounds too high for our ears or the visual picture of the swarm is not yet known. As soon as the female enters the swarm a dark group forms round her, and quite soon the male which has had the luck to snatch the female falls with her to the ground, where mating is completed.

The famous mayflies behave precisely in the same way as the midges, and their occasional mass appearance has excited the imagination of poets of all ages. It is true that for poets propagation was not the all-important problem but sentimental thoughts on the transitoriness of life, which in the imagos of the mayflies often lasts no more than a few hours. The main part of a mayfly's life is passed in a larval state in water.

The mating dances of their males are much more impressive than those of the midges because they are larger and more showy, and with their transparent, gleaming white wings create the impression of whirling snowflakes. The point of view of the spectator will of course affect his judgment. Whoever, on a fine spring evening, when the river is "smoking", unexpectedly finds himself in this kind of "snowstorm" whilst the wretched creatures get into his eyes and up his nose, smother his clothes and make the horses shy will no doubt find less spiritual uplift from this sort of thing than the naturalist who can observe the play of the mayflies in peace seated in a water-meadow near the lake. Like the midges, the mayflies prefer to gather round objects raised a little from the ground, for instance over small alders. Then we see them form dense clouds or pillars which if the breeze freshens are carried off like undulating veils of mist, to re-form over the treetops into more towers of smoke. It is a glimpse of incomparable beauty. Here again the swarms consist only of males, and again one may observe that the females, which are also larger, fly into the swarm individually to be immediately seized upon by a male.

Male choirs

Homer has told the immortal tale of the sirens whose songs attracted men with a magic force. It is remarkable then that in Nature matters are precisely the opposite. The males make music, and the females find it irresistible. We meet this phenomenon in two quite different groups of animals, insects and amphibia.

Amongst the former the chirping of crickets and grasshoppers are the best known. It is well known to anyone who has walked across a meadow in summer or lain in long grass for a spell; one can eavesdrop at close quarters on the concert of these small beings. These performances are less striking than the dances, since they do not form mass concerts but only solos. Each male is his own conductor; he fiddles alone, and the consequence is that eventually a single female approaches him. These things had therefore to be studied in more detail in the laboratory, and to this end wingless species were chosen which can be better controlled.

Incidentally, in all these creatures both male and female possess hearing organs. They are placed, it is true, in a somewhat unusual spot; in grasshoppers on the abdomen, in the tree-cricket and cricket on the front legs. But in both cases the auditory nerve leads to the brain, in which as in us the sensation of hearing arises. To prove with certainty that it is the hearing which draws the infatuated female to the male, one can make use of a little artifice by bringing the musical male into a room by himself and allowing him to sing into a microphone. The receiver which is connected with it should stand in another room. To this we bring the female, and we can now observe that as soon as the sounds emerge she will make a beeline for the receiver. The following diagram (Fig. 15) shows another method. The assertion made here, that in crickets and grasshoppers only the males produce music, cannot be sustained for the field grasshopper. In 1949 Jacobs was able to demonstrate very interesting amœbæan singing between males and females in a whole series of species. The very soft and therefore usually inaudible song of the female is the answer to the song of the male, and a

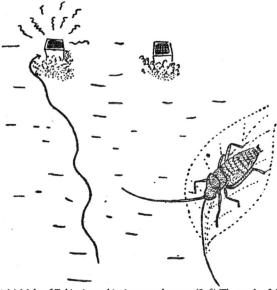

Fig. 15. (*Right*) Male of *Ephippiger ephippiger*, grasshopper. (*Left*) The track of the amorous female leads to the cage of the singing male. The cage of the silenced male is ignored.

sign of her amorousness. The females never sing on their own account, but only in reply to the males. As the male hears these notes he becomes very excited, turns here and there and eventually runs in the direction of the sound. He stops now and again and shrills whilst the female answers, thus the two gradually approach each other. The wooing ceremonies can now, since agreement has already been reached before-hand, be materially abridged.

From this well-authenticated case we may with assurance draw conclusions about the others. In insects musicians are also found among the cicadas and water-bugs. The intolerable notes of the large singing cicadas are better known to the Southern European than to the Northerner. In the south of Europe these large animals, some two inches long, perch on telegraph poles and on any available trees, making a positively fiendish uproar. The females are dumb, a fact that induced the ungallant Greek poet Xenarchos to make the well-known scoffing (paraphrased) verse "Happy are the dear cicadas, for their wives are always dumb". The consequence of their wooing is as difficult to observe as it is in the case of the grasshopper.

In all these, as in the dances of the male midges, we must on no account imagine that the creatures sing with the object of infatuating the females. It is their nature to sing; the females come creeping up also because they must, and when they finally join each other the union does not occur through any sort of design but from an obscure pressure of instinct. It is, however, interesting that the making of music by the male insect has moved one step upward from the bonds of sex. It is plain that the creatures enjoy their own songs and that they mutually encourage each other to perform. This forms, in fact, the basis of the oft-observed and experienced song contest. Lying in a meadow and looking at a cloud, one can very soon make out grasshoppers taking turns at their song. First one sings a couple of bars, then stops, and another immediately takes it up and so on, possibly for quite a long time. A specially perceptive naturalist actually succeeded in insinuating himself into one of these singing contests! The main thing is to strike the right note and not to produce a long-drawn-out sound, but a quick succession of notes as the creatures themselves do in their chirping. Should one succeed in this then the little male will join in and one can contend with him. Sometimes a concert of this sort may come about fortuitously. A German naturalist who was serving his time in the Army noticed when on the parade ground at the Würzburg barracks that the cicadas sitting in the surrounding trees invariably joined in whenever a roll of drums was beaten.

The case of the frogs is too well known for us to go into its details. Actually, it happens precisely as in crickets and grasshoppers. The males croak and the females come swimming along. The song contest is repeated melodiously, and instances are not lacking in which a contest was successfully but accidentally started amongst frogs in the wild. In a house known to me which had a large conservatory, the tree-frogs living there instantly burst into song when some ladies started a lively chatter at the tea-table; a clergyman had to abandon a baptismal address in the same room, because the frogs' competition overpowered his voice. The human voice must remind the frogs a little of their own. Instruments like pianos or violins, on the contrary, never encourage frogs to croak.

6

SEX RECOGNITION

In the previous chapter the question was posed: What means do animals use to attract the opposite sex? There we were dealing with animals which otherwise live by themselves and which must therefore find the females by some specific action. Opposed to these stands the great number of beasts living in communities and those which live so close together that the problem of search does not exist. Here, however, another complication arises. As an example let us take a fish like a stickleback. The male stickleback must be capable of picking out from a swarm of his own kind a gravid female. She must be able to distinguish the uxorious male fish from the others. Before proceeding farther, however, we must answer a very odd question. We humans are "seeing animals" and judge nearly everything round about us by its optical impression on us. What we look like ourselves we can find out in a mirror, and this self-knowledge we can also use to examine human individuals with a more or less kindly criticism and for comparison with ourselves. Savages still have, as a rule, no mirrors and do not really know what they themselves look like, but obviously they can by means of speech ascertain that each looks more or less like the rest of his tribe.

Amongst animals the affair is, however, very much more difficult. Animals which live in herds like cattle or antelopes are comparatively well off, but many other animals, before they begin their own independent lives, see only their mothers and brothers and sisters, and if finally, as in most lizards, the parents take no further interest in the eggs after they have been laid, then the little fellow is quite alone in the world when he leaves his shell. If he belongs to the species of wall lizard, how can he know, when he has reached male maturity and is going courting, what a female wall lizard looks like?

Nature has, at least in the lower forms of life, made use of a very simple aid to overcome this very difficult problem. Recognition of the opposite sex is by observation of easily recognized characteristics. Naturally such recognition is innate, and since courtship sets in in consequence of this recognition animal psychologists have called these characteristics "innate courtship releasing scheme". Latterly, the same animal psychologists have talked of an "innate releasing mechanism" (or I.R.M.). By this they mean the central nervous apparatus which directs the animal's attention to that particular characteristic. Hereafter it must be understood that the male, which is to recognize his mate, need not keep every detail of her appearance in his head. This would be far too complicated. Nature has implanted in him firmly only a few of the more outstanding characteristics of the female as his inheritance for life. These marks or characteristics may be of various kinds, either powerful sensory impressions, for instance a colour, or it may be some feature of the behaviour of the animal which tips the scale. Let us first look at the sensory impressions which here play their part. For the naturalist the easiest way to study this subject is to choose a beast which orientates itself visually. If we wish to study the "innate-scheme female" for our male, we make use of a dummy which first of all resembles the real female as nearly as possible in form, size and colouring. We are then able to vary and simplify all these factors.

In the dragon-fly, *Caloptoryx splendens*, it has in this way been found that the wing span is the most important factor. This size comes to a proportion of 3·3 to 1 of body length in centimetres (1 cm. = ·394 of an inch) in a normal female; the limiting values between which the decoy has been shown to be effective are 3·9 to 2·1 cm. and 2·3 to 0·9 cm. Too large or too small decoys do not function; the shape of the wing on the other hand seems to be a matter of indifference. This is not surprising in view of the poor definition of which the insect's eyesight is capable. The colour also is of great importance. The wings of the female of this species are a delicate green, and have a transparency of some 60 per cent. One can therefore understand that dummies with yellow, red, blue, violet or black wings are disregarded by the male, whereas green, green-yellow and blue-green are successful.

In butterflies we have creatures which see considerably less well than dragon-flies. Most butterflies have colouring and markings which delight our eyes, and we are readily inclined to believe that these characteristics so attractive to us must be those noticed by the ardent butterfly in its love gambols. Whether this is so regarding the colour we do not yet know with certainty; the markings, however, as far as is known at present, seem to have no significance at all. The grayling (*Eumenis semele*), a species of satyr butterfly, which is of course not highly coloured but brown, is attracted neither by the colour, nor by the size, nor by the shape of the proffered object. The only things of importance are that the dummy should be near him, that it should contrast well with the sky and that it should make fluttering movements like a living female. The accompanying illustration shows how the decoy may be varied without reducing its effectiveness (Fig. 16).

FIG. 16. Dummies for the flying courtship of the grayling, *Eumenis semele*, butterfly. The shape has no influence.

In vertebrates also we meet with the same primitiveness. The researches of the celebrated animal psychologist Tinbergen made in 1937 on the stickleback were very illuminating. At mating time the male stickleback is distinguished by a fiery red belly, and the gravid female proclaims herself as such by the thickness of her swollen ovaries. In addition both sexes assume characteristic poses in certain situations. Tests with dummies have shown which are the "key attractions" to which the opposite sex react. Oddly enough the shape of the body plays no part even in those animals which have excellent sight comparable with our own. The quite rough female decoy in Fig. 17 (lower), which to a man cannot possibly look like a stickleback, was made love to much more strongly, owing to its distended abdomen, than the decoy represented in Fig. 17 (upper), which is a far more natural depiction of a female stickleback. For the female the principal characteristic in the male is the red colour. In the pipe-fish *Syngnathus* it was found that the yellow colour of the throat is the most important feature. Although these fish are distinguished by their extreme slenderness, a yellow ball was sufficient to entice an ardent female right across an aquarium.

Even among lizards, which are of very much higher standing, the features necessary to stimulate members of the opposite sex are equally simple. The beautiful green emerald lizards acquire a blue throat at mating time. By this they are instantly recognized, both by other males as possible rivals, as well as by females as bridegrooms. This also can be easily proved by experiments with dummies. More important than the sensory impressions, and more widespread, is the behaviour of the animal. We can illustrate this well by going back to the Middle Ages. For a variety of reasons it was at that time possible to clothe oneself in the dress of the opposite sex. How then could the person suspected of such a trick be unmasked? All manner of devices were used to this end, among them the following: a ball or apple was thrown into the person's lap when seated. In that case men and women generally behave differently. Women, who are accustomed to wear skirts, spread their legs to catch the ball in the width of the skirt; men, used to their trousers, do the opposite, and close their legs to prevent the ball falling between them. The disguised person cannot instantly change this "sex-bound habit", although it is not innate but acquired, and thus gives the secret away.

In the animal kingdom it is often exactly the same. In the mating season both sexes show in many cases a characteristically different

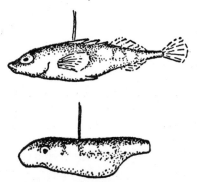

FIG. 17. Dummies of a stickleback female for the analysis of the process of wooing. (*Above*) Facsimile, true to nature, of a female not ardent; (*below*) rough incomplete model of an ardent female with distended ovaries. Details in text.

behaviour, and in this way male can distinguish female and vice versa, even when other sensory stimuli fail. An extreme example of this kind is supplied by fresh-water crustaceans. The American male fresh-water crayfish, in the breeding season, tries to throw every other crayfish it meets on to its back for the purpose of mating with it. The males do not suffer this and defend themselves. The females who are ready to mate do not offer resistance to it. By the different behaviour of the sexes, then, the situation is at once made clear.

Examples of this sort can be found throughout the animal kingdom. In the grayling (*Eumenis semele*), for instance, the lovelorn males attack every butterfly which gets in their way. The other males withdraw from this persecution by flight; the females on the other hand settle on the ground. Among the lower vertebrates and birds the male, when he encounters another of the same species, usually puts on his so-called "dominant attitude", that is to say, he draws himself up to his full height and tries to look as imposing as he possibly can. Fish spread their fins and boast with the colouring of their bodies, lizards strut about stiff-legged, and those able to do so inflate themselves. Birds, for instance the ravens, puff out their feathers and assume the most magnificent appearance that they can. Another male, for whom this gesture is intended, "dominates" in his turn, from which a fight may develop. The females do not do this and thus make known by their timidity to which sex they belong.

Among the higher vertebrates the question as to how the sexes recognize each other is one much more difficult to answer than for the lower. Compared with the lower vertebrates, these animals possess better sensory organs and above all a much more highly developed brain. It may therefore be assumed with certainty that it is much easier for them to recognize each other and that such clumsy means of assistance as red bellies or blue throats, as in the stickleback and emerald lizard respectively, are no longer essential to them. In particular cases this is obvious. Peahens and hen pheasants have really no difficulty in recognizing their cocks. It is, however, very different with the animals showing no sexual dimorphism or in which it is not well developed. We may have great difficulty in distinguishing between a male and a female jackdaw or seagull, but can it be said that similar difficulties exist for the animals themselves?

Where accurate and precise experiments have been made it has invariably been found that birds recognize each other instantly and without any doubt. The yellow bunting has been investigated very closely. In them there is, it is true, something of a sexual dimorphism, but comparing a large number of individuals one finds examples which to our eyes are difficult to distinguish; it may be a female with very pronounced yellow colouring on the head, throat and belly, or it may be a male almost entirely lacking these characteristics of plumage. It has now, however, been established that at least three characteristic-complexes exist through which a certain and immediate distinction between the sexes can be made by the bird. These are the appearance, the song and the behaviour. Each characteristic is sufficient by itself, as a rule, but they can appear together and support each other.

That the visual characteristics are of themselves sufficient can be easily seen if a cage containing two decoy birds, a male and a female, is placed out in a yellow bunting's territory. It will then be observed that each caged bird will only pay attention to the behaviour of one of its own sex outside the cage. When the male in possession of the territory shows himself, the male decoy bird will at once become restless, and defend the cage if the other takes steps to attack it. The female decoy on the other hand remains perfectly calm. If a free female shows herself, the caged one becomes restless whilst the male remains unconcerned.

Similar results can be achieved with stuffed birds. In a particular experiment a female bunting immediately attacked a stuffed female, pecked at it and tore its feathers out, whilst paying no attention to the stuffed male. Blackcocks have also been seen to act in precisely the same way. In fact, they recognize each other instantly. Sex in wildfowl is without doubt recognized immediately by sight.

It can also be assumed with certainty that lizards can distinguish the sexes without difficulty. Gertrud Kitzler states categorically that wall lizards treat cage companions differently according to their sex, which is recognized instantly. Defeated males flee from all other males even if these take no notice of them. Some females may "mince" in front of such males, who continue to behave quite quietly and make no attempt to be "dominant".

Matters are much simpler among the many "scent animals" in which the sense of smell rather than sight predominates. Here is one clear example. In the summer during the night hundreds of various kinds of moths flutter past us, mingling together and all more or less intent on finding mates. There is practically no attempted mating by mistake with members of other species, and among the females there are virtually no old maids. All captured females are found to have been fertilized, and we can only conclude therefore that all the couples find each other by their scent, which must vary from one species to another. Since man is, in his sense of smell, inferior to these creatures, belonging as he does to the microsmatic or "little-smellers", all these things must remain for him a matter for speculation. Precisely the same is found amongst the mammals, which are for the most part macrosmatics or "scent animals". We do not have to wander about in the primeval forests of Africa to be convinced of this. Our most faithful domestic companion, the dog, can most easily teach us the capabilities of his nose.

In all these insects, mammals and other scenting animals, all that the male needs as an innate faculty is to know just this one smell, and he cannot go wrong.

7

COMING INTO BREEDING CONDITION

WHEN we observe the part which each sex has in the matrimonial venture, we meet with a remarkable duplication: the spermatozoon seeks the ovum, the male seeks the female. Both result from the same cause: the active aggressive part seeks the passive, yielding part. As everywhere in biology, so here there are a number of exceptions. In threadworms and crustaceans the spermatozoa are immobile and therefore unable to seek out the ovum; they must be carried to it passively. Also there is a whole series of cases, which will be discussed later, in which the female seeks the male. But even then it is eventually the male which in the transference of the seed takes the active part.

The manner in which the male advances his demand varies very much from species to species and will be discussed in more detail later. In many animals both sexes are ready for mating at all times, and mating takes place immediately the pair meet. This is true, for instance, of some moths. The wingless and unformed female of some moths will be covered immediately by the approaching male the moment she has stepped out of the chrysalis. Since this female is really only an egg-laying machine there is no reason why she should not be ready for mating. The male has therefore to take no special action to induce her to mate.

Apart from these instances, which are in any case rare, it may be said that the way the male conducts himself is dependent essentially on the division of labour. Everywhere when nothing can be gained by force, whether it be that the female is larger and stronger than the male or that the male lacks the weapons to have his way against the will of his mate, the male woos the female; he seeks in some agreeable

Driving roebuck,
with hind.

Immediately before mounting.

PLATE VIII.
Peacock fanning his tail feathers.

Plate IX.
Fiddler crab (*Uca*).

Vipers (Ophidians)
during mating play.

Wall lizard. Pairing
march: female lead-
ing, male following.

PLATE X.
Stag-beetle males
in battle array.

Common vipers during
courtship.

Sexual battle between
two male lizards.

way to make the female compliant. We find this sort of courtship or wooing in numerous groups of animals, not, however, in the lowest. It always presupposes something psychical, for the courted female must dispose of various moods, which she is able to change. In invertebrates we find a typical courtship in many spiders, a number of insects, in octopods and perhaps in some crustacea. In vertebrates it is most impressive and best known in birds, yet is not lacking even in the remaining groups. In the last two decades animal psychology has gone into the question of courtship very thoroughly, and has arrived at the conclusion that in such pairing there is a more or less complicated chain of reactions. Every action on the part of one partner gives rise to a corresponding action on the part of the other. In a manner of speaking, they toss the ball back and forth until mating puts an end to the game.

This has been demonstrated particularly clearly of the stickleback, the behaviour of which may be taken as typical for all pairing phenomena. The male takes over a territory and builds his nest in it. He then waits. The appearance of a female, whose maturity is recognized by the male stickleback by her well-distended belly, induces in him the so-called zigzag dance, a typical courtship dance, in which the male exhibits all his charms, especially his fiery red belly. The dance encourages the female to swim towards the seductive dancer. As soon as the male sees this he ceases to dance, turns and makes a bee-line for his nest. She follows, and this encourages him in his turn to push his head into the nest, an inviting gesture, which causes the female to slip right into the nest. With this, the male strikes her body a series of quick taps with his snout and this eventually causes her to spawn in the nest, whereupon the male fertilizes the eggs.

In the following pages we will have no opportunity to carry out further analogies, but will simply describe the observation, although it should be emphasized that in essence matters proceed similarly in all animals. In the following we will first examine invertebrates in some detail.

(a) COURTSHIP IN INVERTEBRATES

The crustaceans

Let us commence with the crustacea, of which, up to the present, we know very little. We will deal chiefly with tropical species. The gaily coloured males of the tropical crustacean *Callinectes* are said to strut up and down in front of their females during the mating time, with their

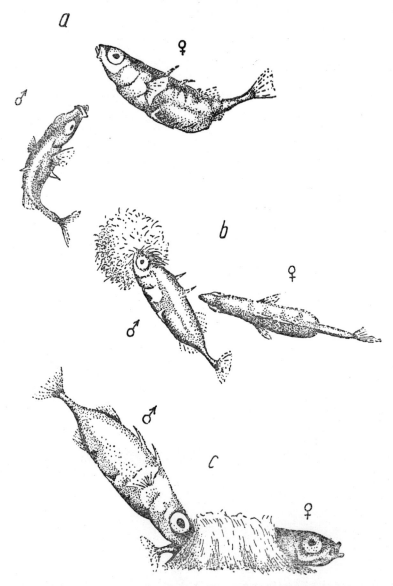

FIG. 18. Three pictures from the courting behaviour of the stickleback: (*a*) zigzag dance of the male stickleback in front of a female; (*b*) male entices the female to the nest; (*c*) the male butting the female, who has slipped into the nest, to induce the depositing of the eggs.

bodies held erect and claws widespread for the purpose of attracting them. This is to a certain extent a preliminary to the singular behaviour of the so-called fiddler crabs (*Uca, Gelasimus*). Amongst these animals, of which numerous species inhabit the sandy coasts of tropical seas, the female's claws are equal in size and serve to shovel in the mud which forms her food. In the male, on the other hand, one claw has attained monstrous size, is usually larger than the body, and generally is vividly coloured. According to the older authors, when a male meets a female during the mating season he is said to exhibit all the signs of the strongest emotion, raising himself high and waving the large claw before her in a crescendo of movement which ends as if he were quite mad. If on this invitation the female approaches him she is seized and led into the mud cavity in which the male normally lives. Whether all this actually happens is still a little doubtful. In a film one can see that the male continually beckons whether there is a female about or not. The waving has therefore perhaps a more generalized meaning, and it is advisable to await further research (see Plate IX).

Dragon-flies

In insects the wooing is more widespread than in crustacea. A case which is very primitive will introduce us to the nature of the courtship ceremonies of these creatures. At the end of May and in a sunny meadow beside a stream one may see certain delicate dragon-flies glide past with a darting flight. They are members of the genus *Calopteryx*. Each male takes up a convenient position in the morning, on a willow or in the meadow, and takes possession of the region round it as his preserve, from which he drives all rivals and also other smaller insects, and awaits the arrival of a heaven-sent female. Should one come along there follows in rapid succession a series of ritual movements which reach their climax in the laying of the eggs by the female. Dragon-flies have good eyesight, and so the male espies the female at a distance of some two yards. He greets the appearance of his prospective mate with an encouraging gesture by spreading his wings repeatedly on the leaf he is occupying and at the same time raising the rear end of his body. When she appreciates this sign language she ends her flight and alights, usually on a floating leaf. Now is the time for him to woo her. He skims close above the water or alternatively sliding on the surface and in a fluttering flight over the point where she is resting, follows if she changes her position and continues this game until she decides finally to remain in one place for a little longer. He has now reached a point where mating can begin.

The courtship of crickets

A short wooing occurs also among crickets and grasshoppers. As we have seen, among these animals, the females are lured by the song of the males. This attraction by the power of music is, however, only the beginning. When the two have so nearly approached each other that they can touch antennæ the male becomes silent. Now the second step begins. After the first brief shock—the creatures remain for a moment after the initial touch as if turned to stone—they commence to feel each other over. Everything is examined, the head, the thorax, the wing covers, the feelers. In this manner, patently through awareness by scent, they recognize a mate. The supreme significance of the antennæ in this game was readily seen when these important organs were removed from a male. The decoy song was produced by the feelerless male exactly as normally. When, however, the female advanced and stroked him with her feelers he took fright and vanished, and no mating took place.

Only when a male has recognized who his partner is does the wooing commence, which again is carried out by song. At first he sings only one bar and retreats a few steps. Then comes the wooing song anew, this time, however, with more bars. Simultaneously the male makes a backwards movement and presses himself against the female, which has followed him. This game of wooing and retreating may be repeated many times until finally mating occurs.

The courtship of butterflies

One of the most appealing and interesting examples of courtship is undoubtedly that of the butterfly. Unfortunately the behaviour of these has been the least investigated. First we are confronted with two problems, one which refers to the silver-washed fritillary (*Argynnis paphia*) and the other to the grayling (*Eumenis semele*). Let us first examine the silver-washed fritillary. This large and beautiful butterfly flies in July and August at the edges of woods or in open glades, where blackberry hedges and other bushes offer the necessary flowers. The courtship can be divided into two phases, on the wing and on the ground. The former occurs naturally, when the male seeks out the female. For this he circles the flowers on which this butterfly is accustomed to sit. The female when found may behave in a variety of ways. If not ready for mating she usually flees and attempts to get out of sight of the male as swiftly as possible. A female which is ready for mating makes the fact known by not flying away but by spreading her wings and fluttering them delicately. Then after some time she takes wing. During this flight the actual flying courtship is performed, which presents a very attractive play. The female flies in a peculiar fluttering flight a few yards above the ground horizontally or gradually rising upwards and preferably over bare patches or other clear surfaces. The male on the other hand carries out a series of remarkable capers. He comes flying from behind, flies below the female and climbs steeply close in front of her to a height of some six inches above her. During

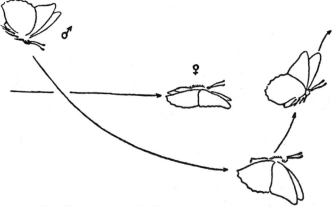

FIG. 19. Courtship of the silver-washed fritillary, *Argynnis paphia*. Flying wooing; ♂ male, ♀ female.

this time she flies beneath and past him, so that as soon as the original position is regained the game recommences. In this way considerable distances up to a hundred yards may be traversed.

Probably the male acts during this flight through his scent scales, which are situated on some of the veins of his forewings, on the chemical sensory organs of the female. This may well only happen during the short phase in which the male flies upwards close in front of the female.

This flying courtship comes to an end when the female alights either on the ground or on a large flower of an umbelliferous plant. The behaviour of the female now changes. She spreads her wings unusually widely so that they lie quite flat, and from time to time raises her abdomen on which there are scent organs, the scent from which heightens the excitement of the male. During this phase the male flies

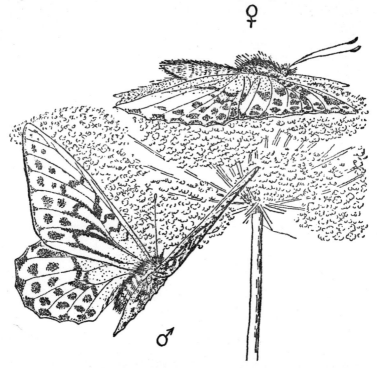

Fig. 20. Courtship of silver-washed fritillary, *Argynnis paphia*. Commencement of ground wooing. The female sits spread out flat on a bloom, the male flies to her.

round in close rings. This game is soon replaced by the third phase, in which the female raises herself somewhat and the male finds a footing next to her, at first at right angles to her. Now we arrive at the so-called bowing of the male, which consists of his bending forward with a powerful jerk and at the same time opening his wings so that the forepart of the female's body comes to lie between them. A very similar game will be found to be played by the grayling. The biological importance of this may consist in the female butterfly possibly coming into contact with the scent scales of the male in a more intimate way than was possible during the courtship flight. During the succeeding period the male becomes a little more obtrusive. At first he drums on the rear wings of the female with his antennæ and middle legs; later he beats the hind wings of the female with the tips of his palps and lays one of his antennæ in a peculiar manner between the antennæ and eyes of the female and strokes them up and down. It is asserted that a special organ lies there, the so-called chætosema, which perhaps responds to such stroking excitation.

With these proceedings the wooing is as good as over, and mating, with which we will deal later, will become imminent.

Now let us turn our attention to the courtship of the grayling (*Eumenis semele*). In his search for the female the male, already very excited sexually, flies towards every other butterfly with great speed. When the male discovers his error he turns away again. This process may go on for several days, for the females of this species always appear a little later than the males. If a female of the same species is flown at as

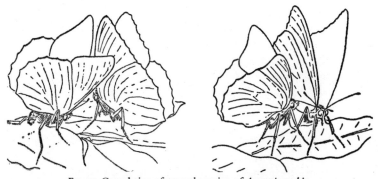

FIG. 21. Completion of ground wooing of *Argynnis paphia*.

described, she will usually alight on the ground after a short chase. The enchanting courtship flight is therefore not carried out. The male settles in the closest proximity to the female, usually behind her. Then, however, he goes round her in a semicircle so that the two finally face each other head to head. A series of ceremonies now follows which we can only examine briefly: the wing flirting, the fanning and the antennæ-twisting. In this latter the male spreads his feelers across the length of his body horizontally, and commences some remarkable contortions in which the feelers describe a cone. What the meaning of this may be is not yet quite clear, but the succeeding phase, the bowing, is fairly easy to explain. The male spreads both pairs of wings and bends the forewings very far forward. By flapping the wings together he brings the female's feelers into the immediate vicinity of the scent scales, which in this species lie on a larger area of the forward wings. In *Satyrus fidia* I observed, during this phase, a rhythmic bumping on the part of the male with his head against that of the female. After the bowing the male again walks in a semicircle round the female and places himself behind her. With this the wooing game is practically finished.

In many butterflies the males are distinguished from the undecorative females by magnificent colours. It may be assumed with certainty that with them the wooing takes place by visual stimuli, but we know nothing about it yet. Altogether, little is known to us of the courtship of insects, and we will therefore turn to another group of animals, the spiders.

The courtship of spiders

In spiders the wooing is extraordinarily widespread, a fact that is obviously connected with the female's combativeness and often larger size, so that all possibility of using force is denied to the male. In spite of this, wooing does not occur with all species. In the wolf spider (*Lycosa pullata*) the male immediately runs to the female and mating takes place without any preliminaries. These are, however, rare exceptions.

For the rest, each family, often each species, has its own peculiarities, of which we shall examine at least a few in somewhat more detail. In wolf spiders, with which we will start, there are many species, like *Lycosa saccata*, which indulge in all sorts of manœuvres with their palps. As soon as the male catches sight of the female, which he does at a quite respectable distance, since these creatures have excellent sight, he raises the fore part of his body and beckons with his palps. After this exercise he advances a couple of paces towards her, and in some particular cases he may describe a complete circle round the female of his desire. Other wolf spiders carry out corresponding exercises with their feelers.

The courtship movements of the jumping spiders, which have even better sight, are also very entertaining. Here the wooing begins with the male turning towards the female by a sort of jerky movement and then running towards her. At a distance from her of about two inches he raises his fore-part steeply and, with his front pair of legs uplifted high, makes distinct beckoning movements. This beckoning obviously serves as a sign language which the female understands. If she is not ready for mating she will run away. Should she, however, be willing to consent she will remain quietly seated, and at this point the actual love dance will commence. It consists in the male making a peculiar zigzag

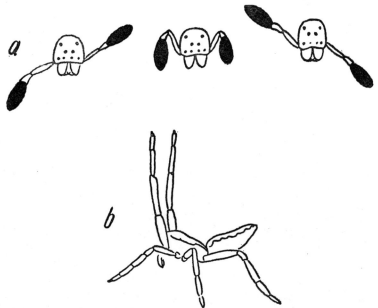

Fig. 22. Wooing position of various wolf spiders: (a) *Lycosa saccata*, viewed from in front; (b) another wolf spider from the side.

run, with body slantingly raised, with the object of arriving in position opposite the female, head to head. At last the male has pushed forward in this way to within half an inch, and if she still does not move then he can risk taking her by storm (Fig. 23).

Things go very differently with the orb spiders. Sight here has nothing to do with it, and everything is through feeling. The male first discovers the female probably through his sense of smell. The orb spiders as a rule make use of soft mechanical stimulants to rouse the female sitting in her citadel. Generally the males spin two threads from their original position to the periphery of the female's web and then start to pluck at the threads rhythmically. In other cases, especially when the female is not at the centre of her web but somewhere near its edge, the males will venture boldly on to the female's web itself and there start gently tugging the threads which lead towards the keep. The picture as usually presented in books is somewhat out of date and lacks the necessary precision. An exact analysis does not, in fact, exist in every case. Nevertheless, we will present in the following one of these

FIG. 23. Love dance of jumping spider, *Epiblemum scenicum*, in front of a dead, motionless female.

older accounts, in which fact and fiction are agreeably mingled. It concerns *Filistata insidiatrix*. "Between the two animals a peculiar and complicated sort of telegraphy is developed. The male creeps on to the web and pulls firmly at the threads with his cheliceræ. He shakes it impatiently, moves forward a little, retreats again and circles cautiously round the citadel of the female. These are, as one can see, in his clumsy speech, real amorous entreaties. This the female answers by plucking in her turn at the threads and, to wit, in such a manner that it becomes quite obvious. The connection between the two is now established, a real exchange of sentiment, but transmitted entirely by sensory excitation. Finally after half an hour, the female decides to emerge a little from her concealment. This is, however, not yet enough and she is compelled to come out on to the web entirely. Now he fondles her with his fore-legs and takes her by the hand, if I may be allowed to use this expression, which is nevertheless quite exact. I have often seen how he has laid her fore-claws in his and has drawn her tenderly towards him. Sometimes she accepts it with fear and withdraws into her place of concealment; in that case he recommences the game." (Berland.)

It does not quite fit this touching account that, after the mating, and precisely amongst these orb spiders, the female makes short work of her mate, on which subject we will have more to say. This "holding hands" is explained by modern science as an action to prevent the female striking with her murderous poisoned claws, for it is true that the male holds them fast (see Fig. 24). There are, however, cases in which the male spiders behave somewhat vigorously. This is so among the rare crab spiders, which in general run about freely. The females here are much bigger than the males. Should an ardent male encounter a female he will creep on her back with great agility and without beating about the bush. There he will be fairly safe from attack by her. They often then roll about together, and as soon as she desists from repulsing him he will instantly regain his position on her back.

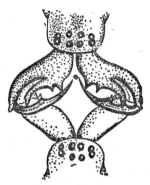

FIG. 24. Spider, *Pachygnatha clercki*, seizing of the poison fore-claws (cheliceræ) of female by the male before mating.

This, however, can hardly be called a wooing; the only thing which could be called by that name is perhaps the beating movement executed by him whilst squatting on her back.

The wedding gift

It is very remarkable that among the arthropods, namely among insects and spiders, another habit has developed which is otherwise found only in some birds, that is, the presentation of a wedding present by a courting male.

As an introduction we will first consider the behaviour of the male spiders of the *Meta segmentata* and *Nephila brasiliensis* species. With them mating takes place only when the female has a captured animal in her web. The logic of this event is very obvious. The female, so dangerous to the male, is so occupied with her prey that she becomes conscious of the presence of the male without attacking him. The course of events need not be always the same. At first the position is that the female sits in the middle of the circular web and the male, having spun a "wooing thread" towards her, is at the periphery. Then, when a fly flies into the web it is either snatched first by the nimbler male and cocooned, or it may also happen that the female seizes it. The end is no doubt in either case the same. The male operates in both cases under the protection of the cocooned fly and thus is able to approach the female.

The contrary is the case with *Pisaura listeri*, where the male always presents the fly to the female as a wedding gift. He catches it, spins it into a spherical lump, seizes it with his cheliceræ and carries it in to the quiescent female. The procedure may last quite a long time. Often the female flees. In other cases she behaves entirely passively and does not

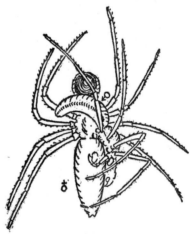

Fig. 25. Mating of a *Pisaura* spider. The female devours the silk-shrouded insect; during this the male carries out the mating.

accept the proffered fly. The male on the other hand shows all the signs of great excitement, vibrating the hind part of his body and shaking his outstretched feelers. When the female finally grabs the fly, the male takes advantage of her preoccupation with the prey to come cautiously to the position for mating.

Amongst the insects, the family of two-winged flies known as empids has acquired a certain renown. The entire course of action is very similar to that of the spider. The ardent male catches a very small fly, contrives a peculiar network round it which usually assumes the shape of a balloon, and presents it as a wedding gift. It is interesting that in this large family, which comprises some 3,000 species in all, the whole thing has become an empty ceremonial which yet indicates a necessary prelude to mating. The balloon also does duty, in some species, even if it is empty. Again in other cases it may happen that an insect has indeed been spun in but is completely disregarded by the female. In some species, however, the insect is consumed, by the female alone during mating, or by both the lovers sharing in the enjoyment of it.

The consumption of the prey during mating may be observed also in the remarkable neuropteran (*Bittacus tipularius*). Here, however, there is no question of a wedding gift, the male inviting himself to the snack.

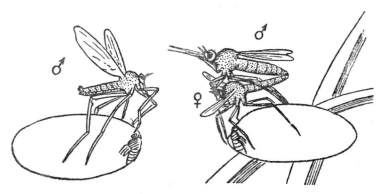

FIG. 26. A species of empis fly: (*left*) balloon-carrying male, (*right*) mating. The balloon was delivered to the female.

He approaches a female who is just on the point of devouring her prey and knows how to arrange cunningly to combine business with pleasure.

The courtship of cuttlefish

Amongst the invertebrates we must not overlook the wooing of the male cuttlefish (*Sepia*). These peculiar creatures have exceedingly well-developed eyes which in their structure resemble those of a fish or other vertebrate. They are therefore as much "visual animals" as fishes, and it is thus self-evident that the courtship is of an optical nature. The male cuttlefish tries to impress his chosen one by his beauty. Usually, it is true, little enough is seen of this beauty. When the *Sepia* is buried in the sand and waiting for his prey, he is as grey as mud. Once he is excited, however, be it by seeing a crustacean which is his favourite food, or that, in the mating season, he meets another cuttlefish, then the *Sepia* puts on a striped dress in a trice, which does not yield in the least in beauty to that of a tiger or a zebra. Purple-black stripes which can change from second to second stand out sharply from a white background, and a peculiar greenish sheen, emanating from certain iridescent cells lying in the tissues beneath the skin, make the whole especially impressive. When the male cuttlefish woos a female something else is added. The fourth arm on the right-hand side, the so-called hectocotylus, is developed as a sexual arm, with the help of which the spermatophores are transferred. This specially wide and beautifully marked arm is offered by the male to his intended. Here the affair goes as will be seen again in fish and other vertebrates. The two sexes are distinct in the manner in which they react to the offer of these festal garments. Another ardent male will reply with the same coin, and they will then mutually try to cut each other out; an ardent female on the contrary does not adorn herself in a gay dress, but remains quite placid.

Unfortunately up to now we have information about the *Sepia* only, and but little about the numerous other cuttlefish which bustle about the oceans. That courtship is with them also of the visual kind seems to be in no doubt. It is told how in the South some fishermen catch the ardent cuttlefish by sinking a mirror, surrounded by all sorts of sharp hooks, in the sea. The creature sees his reflected image and falls upon it, believing it to be a rival or a female, thereupon he is impaled on the maze of hooks and is hastily pulled up.

(b) COURTSHIP IN THE VERTEBRATES

In vertebrates courtship is very unequally distributed. In this group of animals it can be seen especially clearly that a courtship is found only where the use of force does not lead to the desired end. It is most widely distributed amongst birds; in cold-blooded, or poikilothermous, animals it may have a wide distribution, even though it is in many cases so diminished that it hardly merits the name. In mammals, finally, it is almost wholly absent.

Some of the most important ceremonies are similar in fish, lizards and birds. At the first meeting with a female, the male is pleased to assume the so-called "dominant attitude" which consists in making himself as personable as possible. He will, however, also make this gesture in face of other males, and it must therefore on the whole be regarded as asexual. Another male reacts to it in the same measure; he becomes dominant in his turn. Following this, either a fight may ensue or else a friendly attitude. The female shows the counter-dominant at most for only a brief time and reverts then to a strictly specific female behaviour.

In the literature the difference in the behaviour of the two sexes is sometimes put down as a sign of the inferiority of the female sex. It may be so when the male sex is, *eo ipso*, the more powerful physically as in most mammals, and also in some birds. This is confirmed by a new proof, that is to say, that in female monkeys the submissive attitude depends on the sexual cycle. An all-embracing application of this explanation can hardly be claimed. As is well known this "dominant attitude" is met with in human lives. Heinroth once pointed out that a young man who rides a motor-cycle crashes twice as often when his beloved is in the vicinity than otherwise. Such an instinctive expression of power does not mean in the sign language of the lovers: I am stronger than you, therefore when you marry me you must obey me, otherwise there will be trouble. Such a courting would hardly be very clever.

It happens, however, that a young girl prefers a well-grown handsome young man to one who is not good-looking. On this female instinct the instinctive show of strength by the man is based, and it is understandable that we should make a similar assumption for the other vertebrates. The dominant attitude of male vertebrates has therefore a double meaning; *vis à vis* other males it is intended to intimidate, but against females it is seductive.

Fishes

The typical instinctive actions which in vertebrates lead to mating are already present among fishes, and these have been observed in the numerous species examined. First, let us see what happens in the case of cichlids. When at mating time a male sees a female, he immediately shows his full dress and, for the rest, carries out exactly the same movements as for a meeting with another male. He spreads his fins and gill-covers and beats the water with his tail-fins, swimming round the female in high excitement and always showing his broadside. The female has meanwhile not been idle, but has also shown her best dress and answered the beats of the male's tail-fin with similar actions. Nevertheless, this dominant attitude is very soon abandoned by her. After only a few tail movements by the male she closes her fins to her sides. In a male this would be an acknowledgement of inferiority and usually the beginning of flight. The female is distinguished from such a male by continuing to exhibit her gay apparel and in this manner shows her sex.

With that the preliminaries are ended.

On the conclusion of these actions, the female will follow the male and frequently squeeze close to his flank, which may be termed clinging. The next thing that happens is the search for a suitable spawning-ground. It seems that in this the female takes the lead to a certain extent. Anyhow, she carries out the first actions which indicate what is to follow. She stops, namely at some spot or other, and, constantly watched by the male, goes through certain downwards movements at great speed while keeping a vertical position. This seems to be a symbolic action, which simulates the clearing of the future spawning-ground and indicates her mood to the male.

When a suitable spot seems to have been found both partners commence to clear away all foreign bodies as far as possible. This they do chiefly with their bulging lips. There follows a further series of "symbolic actions". This is a rather difficult concept to convey. By "symbolic actions" animal psychologists understand an instinctive action the original meaning of which has been lost. Thus no cleaning or tidying is done, and during the symbolic spawning not a single egg is laid, but the animal behaves as if they had been. The whole thing seems only to have the biological meaning of bringing her partner into a mood similar to her own. We could almost regard this as a sign language which tells the other "I am ready to marry you". Finally a definite spawning-ground is chosen and now there is a real cleaning and polishing till the place is spotless. In addition every other live being, if not too big, will be attacked and driven off by the couple. The male occupies himself mainly in preparing a hollow in which the female will lay the eggs.

Amongst the pipefishes the wooing oddly enough devolves partly or wholly on the female, a preliminary which we otherwise know only in a few birds. It is most remarkable in the pipefish (*Nerophis ophidion*), in which the male remains passive until the end.* In this species the female assumes a true wedding dress, as is usually done only by the males. She shows vivid blue somewhat ramified stripes on her flanks. Further, there develops in mid-belly a yellow ridge of skin one-twelfth of an inch high. The males show, as the only sign of readiness

* I am indebted for these remarks to the kindness of Herr Fiedler of Munich, and for which I thank him.

to spawn, a yellow mouth-tube. The yellow colour has an extraordinarily stimulating effect on the female and causes her to initiate the courtship movements. As soon as an ardent female catches sight of such a male she swims up to him and shows him by all sorts of movements how lovely he is. She then swims in front of him with her head inclined downwards, and he follows all her movements. Finally, the female lies on her side whilst the male lies above her, and in this position they swim forwards. The last part of this love game occurs after they have risen to the surface. The female starts to wrap herself round the male by circular tail movements. These tactile agitations generate an intense excitement and lead immediately to the laying of the eggs and to the emission of milt.

In sea-horses (*Hippocampus brevirostris*) the courtship is shared to some extent by both partners. "Animals of both sexes full of spawn swim with dragging tails along the sea-bed and approach others of their species. The males carry their heads drooping on their breasts and blow the pectoral pouch up so that it may even become translucent. Both sexes in their excitement make their flanks pale to a silvery shade of colour; sometimes one can even see the swim-bladder showing through. Whilst the sea-horses swim alongside each other over the sea-bed they embrace each other with their tails, incline to both sides and rock from side to side. This swim is followed by rising to the surface. It is initiated by a very characteristic instinctive movement of the female. She lifts up her head with a jerk so that it forms an obtuse angle with the long axis of the body. The male thereupon continually presses his tail forward ventrally by strokes; this pressure squeezes the pouch and liquid is driven out of it. Thus the couple rise either vertically beside each other or else turn together head to head and circle round each other, like a merry-go-round, during their upward swim. On reaching the surface they swim about alongside each other, during which their coronellæ are mostly slightly above water. As a rule the couple now incline their anal regions towards each other and the female endeavours to touch the male lightly with her orange-coloured genital papilla, which projects forward about one tenth of an inch. These attempts at transferring the ova are repeated frequently by the female. When the males are in spawning mood they squeeze the pouch at frequent intervals by pressing the tail against its bottom and thus compressing it ('pumping'). The transference of the ova takes place during the surface swim or whilst rising. The female thrusts her genital papilla into the almost pea-sized pouch opening of the male, the couple standing turned head to head with tails curved backward in a bow, as a rule for ten seconds. The eggs are laid directly into the pouch of the male by the female during this union and there they are immediately fertilized by him."*

The amphibians

The two main groups of the vertebrate amphibia class, the Anura and the Urodeles (tailless and tailed amphibians), are distinguished fundamentally from each other in their courtship as in everything else. In frogs and toads we can hardly speak of a courtship. As is well known, the females react to the love croaking of the males by swimming towards them. The males for their part only address an approaching female directly when she moves.

In newts the mating is preceded by a typical love game which may be called a wooing. Only in the most primitive, the Hynobiids, does a similar prelude seem to be absent. In *H. lichenatus* from Japan the search for a suitable spawning place begins as soon as the animals have found each other. On a suitable stone the female will lay a mass of eggs which the male then inseminates. The whole process, although it takes place ashore, is similar to that of some fish.

The much observed and described wooing of our newts is initiated probably by certain sensory perceptions, which may well originate from the ardent females giving off some sort of scent into the water. The males swim hither and thither and accost every being or object of suitable size. Having found a female they assume a very character-istic attitude which consists in placing themselves squarely across her path. Peculiar tail movements follow which are called "beating" and probably serve various purposes: to show off the gay coat, which is most conspicuous on the tail, and perhaps also to provide mechanical and chemical excitation. It has been asserted over and over again that the male produces a scent which is given off into the water by glandular elements of the rear wall of the cloaca. This has not been definitely proved. Specific differences show themselves only in the extent and rhythm of these movements and in a few other details. Thus the males of *Triton cristatus* and *T. boscai* stroke the females on the tip of the snout with the flat of the tail when they "beat". *T. marmoratus*, on the other hand, does it with the tip of the tail.

In any case these movements last for hours without intriguing the

* By letter from Herr Fiedler.

female. When at last she is ready for mating she reacts with the so-called "imitative reaction". She strides slowly up to the male; and this changed attitude is for him a signal to change his also. He takes a sudden swift turn and runs slowly away in a so-called "waddling step". In this step or walk the body, particularly the cloacal region, is dragged along close to the ground. At some convenient spot the male now plants a spermatophore on the ground. The female, closely following, then picks the spermatophore up in her cloaca as she steps over it.

The reptiles

Among the lizards, again, the mating game starts with the now well-known "dominant attitude" of the male. It consists in the creature stalking along stiff-legged and at the same time holding his head up and back, an attitude which reminds us rather of a horse on the curb. Further, the ribs are so disposed as to exhibit the largest possible surface of body to his mate. This has the added advantage of bringing the vivid colouring of throat, flank and belly into view (see Plate V).

The females react variously according to whether or not they are ready to mate. Those which are ready reply by "stamping" and tail-quivering. The former consists in the female turning her head to the male and stamping the ground in quick time with her fore-feet. The tail-quivering is an undulating movement of the tail in a horizontal direction. The stamping is also done by males, but only when they have been beaten in a fight with another male. It may well be a sign of submission. In the biology of mating it is very significant that in ardent females these two reactions of stamping and tail-quivering occur only very faintly or not at all. This proves that the female behaviour does not indicate any inferiority. An ardent female will avoid the male, with or without stamping, and run slowly away. This running away, however, is not a flight; unwilling females on the contrary run away at such a speed that the pressing suitor cannot overtake them. With the ardent female, however, the movement is so dilatory that one gets a definite impression that she wishes to be over-taken. In these circumstances the male can follow comfortably, his snout remaining generally about half a tail's length in front of her tail-tip, which gives him the opportunity to lick the female frequently. The whole of this ceremony may be called a "pairing march" (see Plate IX). After a while the female goes more and more slowly and at last it comes to the male literally having to push the female in front of him. Gradually he catches up on her and when his head has reached the vicinity of the root of her tail he moves forward smartly to execute the flank bite which precedes actual mating.

It is of interest that in lizards no overpowering ever occurs. "The female flees when unwilling, with an alacrity equal to that of a beaten male from his conqueror, and races away in yard-long hops, very different to the short runs of the ardent and willing one, where the male is waited for by the female. The male never returns the bites of the unwilling females angrily, be they ever so violent." (Kitzler, 1941.)

The birds

The courtship behaviour of birds has been studied most intensively of all. The large number of species in this group of animals and the extreme variety of their behaviour has also enabled us to gain a somewhat deeper insight into the nature of these remarkable instinctive

FIG. 27. *Pygoscelis adeliæ*, penguin, courtship. The female stands in the scraped-out nest cavity.

actions. If we begin with a description of outward manifestations it may be said that, in courtship, the most varied means are employed. The best known is naturally the song. Next comes the exhibition of gay plumage, as seen, say, in the peacock. In rarer cases the male assumes, during the wooing, quite remarkable bodily attitudes or, by inflating air-bladders or by the swelling up of blood-filled flaps, makes himself look especially important. These are only the most outstanding cases. With strong flyers we occasionally find a courtship flight, best known in the snipe, and this is coupled with the making of peculiar sounds.

The most pronounced courtship behaviour in the male is always to be observed in those cases in which a strong sexual dimorphism is present. In all these the female behaves more or less passively. This changes, however, when the plumage in both sexes approaches similarity. Then the courtship is often not an exclusively male activity, but is shared by both sexes. The most famous example of this is afforded by the great crested grebe (*Podiceps cristatus*). The various

FIG. 28. Great crested grebe, *Podiceps cristatus*. Mutual wooing play in two distinct phases: (1) cat-pose; (2) penguin dance.

attitudes assumed by the animals in their courtship play are entirely the same for male and female. Fig. 28 shows two phases, first the so-called "cat pose" in which the animals remain opposite to each other head to head, and then the second phase which consists in both fetching vegetable matter from the bottom of the water and presenting it to each other. This is called the "penguin dance". It has been observed that the courtship play is by no means always initiated by the male, but, according to their mood, by one or the other.

These examples lead us gradually to those in which the female is, throughout, the active partner. Here the painted quail is the most given to polyandry; that is, the females have a number of mates. In the painted quail (*Turnix varia*) the courtship has been described as follows: "The male cowers in the short grass and the female runs in a circle round her mate with tail lifted and inflated throat. She then stands still and commences to coo and to purr (exactly like a pigeon luring his female), at the same time stamping and scratching with her feet. Meanwhile the male replies in soft whimpering tones." In this species the female is larger, stronger and more colourful than the male. Things here are thus completely reversed.

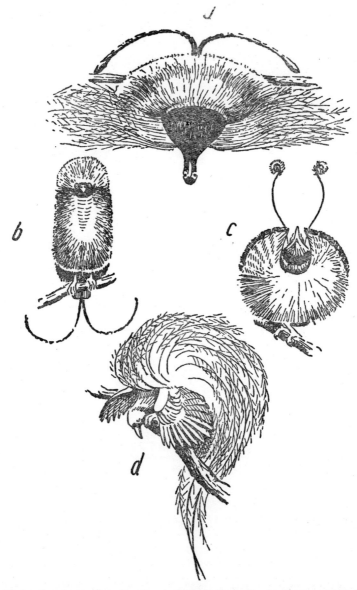

FIG. 29. Courting posture of various male birds of paradise: (a) *Paradisea rudolfi*, bird stands on his head; (b) *Diphyllodes magnificus*, every feather on head and breast stand erect; (c) *Cicinnurus regius*, looking at the bird's throat; (d) *Paradisea minor*.

Precisely as in the lower animals so with birds also we must bear in mind first of all that we are dealing with instincts which, given a certain psychic condition, are carried out with violence, the birds certainly being unaware of their meaning.

Whether the male wishes to look imposing to the female, if his object is to make the female willing to mate, will be concealed from us to eternity. Certain it is, however, that the bird sings because at mating time sing he must. This was understood above all naturalists by "der alte Fritz" (Frederick the Great), with his clear intellect, as at the end of the Seven Years War he wrote in a despairing mood to a friend: "The ox must plough, the nightingale must sing, I must make war." In this sentence there are three categorical imperatives. With the ox it is the whip of the farmer, with the King inescapable fate, with the nightingale the compulsion exercised by the organism through the ductless glands.

In the following we will examine a little more closely a few of the better-known examples of courtship in birds. For the layman the easiest means of providing himself with the enjoyment which this performance yields is to visit a zoological garden in the spring and stand in front of the pheasantry (see Plate VI). The males of the golden pheasant, the silver pheasant and the diamond pheasant possess a special ornament in the beautifully coloured collar which they can raise and lower. For hours on end the cock strolls up and down in front of the hen and at the same time raises his collar in such a manner that she can behold it in its full glory. When he marches from right to left he erects the right-hand side of his collar, the side away from the female, so that she may get the benefit of both sides. As soon as he about turns to retrace his steps from left to right of her he lays the right side down and erects the left. The layman who views this will be almost more impressed by a second phenomenon, to wit the apparently complete indifference of the female, who does not even follow his movements with her eyes and indeed acts as if the whole affair had nothing whatever to do with her. Probably this impression will only have been made because the play of movement of animals in a cage cannot completely work out. It is therefore of value that as a result of an excellent study by Heinroth we have the best of information about the peacock. The courting actions of the peacock consist, of course, in his spreading the tail, an imposing spectacle even to a man (see Plate VIII). When he is in a courting mood this occurs whenever a peahen approaches him, pecking at the ground. When she comes near a highly remarkable reaction takes place, in which the cock about turns and shows her his less beautiful rear side. Now, however, comes the hen's reaction, of the greatest importance for the cock. If she is ready for mating she will run swiftly round the tail to be able to see it from the front again. The cock responds to this with a loud rustling produced by rubbing his feathers together. Thereupon he will turn about again and the game will be repeated several times. At last the peahen will give him to understand that she is ready by lying down in front of him.

To the peacock we may add the argus pheasant, which during his courtship presents one of the most outstanding figures in the animal world and is distinguished from the peacock by having his four hundred "eyes", which give the impression of a row of balls in perspective, not on his tail but on the wing feathers. In this wooing, three phases may be distinguished. First there is a sort of preliminary approach, in which the male runs after the female in great excitement and then tries to get in her way. This preliminary is followed by the principal courting activity which consists in the bird spreading his wings wide with a jerk and flapping them forward so that they form a kind of funnel, which is held in front of the female. In the middle of the "funnel" a small hole remains open through which the head of the bird is seen looking excitedly at her, who on her part, as always in pheasants, seems to be quite uninterested. In this almost unbelievable attitude the male now begins to execute dance movements which constitute the third phase of the play. They consist chiefly of a series of curtseys in which the body sways between a horizontal and a vertical position.

The courtship behaviour of the turkey gives more the impression of a fit of fury. The wings trail on the ground, the tail is erected to a fan, the entire plumage is ruffled up, the fleshy naked places on the neck swell up and glow in fiery colours. In addition there is the peculiar cry, which sounds more like a war-cry than the cooing of a lovelorn swain. I remember it from my early days as sounding rather like "gowder, gowder, gowder". The cock ruffles his plumage sometimes even when he is alone, but mostly when there are hens present. Exactly as in the peacock no particular hen is singled out, but his call is directed to all mateless hens and means something like: "Come, I am ready." Then one of the hens will detach herself from the rest and describe a circle round the strutting cock with a peculiar mincing gait, finally lying down in front of him.

In the examples just discussed the choice has been obviously the female's, who offers herself to the male, and not the male who courts a particular female. On the whole it seems that in birds the former is the more frequent, as is emphasized by the next two examples.

In the night heron the male starts off by choosing a suitable mating-place which he then proceeds to defend against other males. Whilst starting on the nest-building the enticement of the female also occurs by means of a distinctive decoy call. What happens is that a female in the neighbourhood replies to this call and flies near. Only now does the actual courtship begin, in which both sexes take part, having a more or less equal share in the ceremonies. Another very interesting example is furnished by the ruffs and reeves, peculiar plover-like birds which are common in the Northern European lowland plains where it is marshy. The situation is not the same here, inasmuch as numerous males enter the matrimonial lists simultaneously. The creatures seem to have certain courting spots to which they resort year after year. There at a given time a large number of these gather and two males, or ruffs, engage in battle. Whereas the females, or reeves, wear the inconspicuous plumage of a normal plover, the ruffs possess a large erectable collar which is their most important ornament. It is worthy of notice that no two ruffs are alike. In one, for instance, the collar may be dappled black and white, in another perhaps it is partially rust red or dark green, or it may be striped or otherwise marked in the most varied manner. The fight generally ends without bloodshed; it is a ceremonial tourney, at which the hens sit round in a circle as interested spectators and at which they pick the most handsome male. When the battle is over one of the hens will enter the ring, march up to her choice and give him to understand: "Here I am." It has been observed that a particularly fine cock was picked out thrice in one forenoon, whilst some other inconspicuously coloured ones went empty away. Here then we have ladies' choice at its purest. In the same category as these tournaments are also no doubt to be counted the peculiar dance ceremonies to be seen among a few tropical birds. Their connection with sexual life is probable, although not fully proved. Schomburgk reports the following about the South American cock-of-the-rock (*Rupicola aurantia*): "A whole company of these splendid birds held their dance on the smooth and even surface of an enormous rock, and I saw to my great joy a longed-for wish so unexpectedly fulfilled. On the bushes surrounding the rock some twenty admiring spectators, both male and female, sat quite openly whilst the flat surface of the rock was traversed in all directions by one of the males with the most curious steps and movements. Soon the droll bird half spread his wings, moved his head violently in all directions, at the same time brushing the hard stone with his wings, jumped up and down in one spot, sometimes slowly, sometimes quickly, then soon after spread his tail in a fan and with a proud strut again marched about on the flat, until at last he seemed to tire, uttered a strange cry, unlike his usual tones, flew up to the nearest branch and so gave up his place to another male; who in his turn showed off his skill and grace in dancing and who again made way for yet one more performer."

Whereas in the ruffs and reeves and the cock-of-the-rock the creatures appear in company, the remarkable bower-birds, which have been observed with astonishment by many naturalists in Australia and New Guinea, execute a solo dance. There is a whole range of them, each species having its own peculiarities. In one thing, however, they all agree; the male always goes to a great deal of trouble to prepare a special courting-place. This is described very graphically by the New Guinea naturalist Detzner. He says: "Soon the ground had been completely cleaned and the male strutted about satisfied and admiring his work. Here a dry leaf remained to be picked up, there a fibre of root to pull up. Finally off he flew. Next day I was able, with renewed astonishment, to see him at the second stage of his activity. On this day there was a continual coming and going, up to the tree-tops, into the dense scrub of the underbrush, and back again to scatter a few more pieces of dried twigs which he had broken off in the jungle. After a few hours the place looked as if a conifer had shed its needles all over it. The eager bird now vanished for some time, to return with a mass of white forest blooms in his beak, which he heaped in the middle of the space. Only now did the female appear. At first she gazed from a neighbouring low tree upon the dancing movement, accompanied by wild croaking, of the male. She then came flying along and took her place at the heap of flowers and accompanied the more and more excited leaps of the male by soft little tripping steps. Day after day I enjoyed watching the love play of this enchanting pair, the black male with the gold hoop decorating his head, whose breastplate shimmers in all colours and from whose ears three long feathers hang down on each side and which are only feathered on the outer tips of their quills. The female wears a chocolate brown plumage devoid of any ornament."

The species observed by Detzner is, unfortunately, not known. In the tooth-billed cat-bird (*Scenopoetes dentirostris*) the entire dance stage is laid with certain kinds of leaves by the male after having been thoroughly cleaned. These he provides by sawing partly through the stems with his beak. They are all laid with great care, so that the paler side faces upward. Much might also be said of the special ornamental objects used. Not only flowers are fetched along; some species prefer many-coloured stones, parrot feathers, glass splinters, scraps of paper and so on. Human civilization has thus enabled these birds greatly to extend their repertoire.

Some of the birds, as their name implies, first fashion a leafy bower, beginning by placing two rows of dry twigs, inclined towards each other, in the ground, so that a structure arises resembling the roof of a house. In front of the leafy passage the dance floor is cleared. Detzner describes one instance in which the male made no bower but placed a little tree in the middle of the prepared space.

"First he sticks a twelve-inch-high dry twig upright in the ground, and then drags from round about pieces of twig of all manner of lengths which he places together with great skill, joining the stems in such a fashion that the structure looks exactly like a tiny though withered pine tree. And all this trouble just for the sake of pleasing his mate. When the work of art is completed she comes flying up, inspects it and then executes a dance round the 'little tree' with its builder, for which the necessary freedom is provided by the cleared space. Their leaps and wing beats become more and more excited, a game of catch-as-catch-can ensues and finally the male's pertinacity has its reward."

Out of a number of cases in which the courtship is intended for one particular female, we will first describe that of the common raven, to which Lorenz devoted a thorough study. The raven belongs to those birds in which both sexes look alike and are also almost alike in size. In these birds both sexes show instinctive actions. Nevertheless in Nature, in normal cases, these will soon turn out to be of a quite distinct character in the two sexes. The game always begins with both the birds, on first meeting, trying to look imposing to each other, or perhaps it would be better put by saying that they instinctively assume an attitude which seems like a preparation for an imminent battle. When two males meet, a high degree of excitement gradually develops. During this phase the previously ruffled plumage, which gives the bird a particularly magnificent appearance, is again smoothed, except that, on the head, two feathered ears are formed. Having arrived at this stage the two combatants fly at each other and belabour each other with their sharp claws. On the other hand should a male and a female meet it is easy to see that the female loses her dominant attitude and retreats from the advancing male without, however, fleeing as the weaker male would. In the literature on animal psychology different opinions are expressed as to how each animal actually recognizes each other's sex.

FIG. 30. Wooing of common raven: (a) dominant attitude; (b) choking or retching movement; (c) male (*right*) at height of retching movement, female retreating.

Some observers seem to assume that only the different behaviour shows the male that he is confronted by a female. I hold this conclusion to be quite impossible owing to its unbelievably elementary nature. I am convinced that the male bird recognizes the female instantly and with certainty before he gets near her.

The play of movement in which the male advances and the female slowly retreats may last some time, and the birds may cover considerable distances in this way. Both make continuous peculiar bows during this time and utter characteristic notes. Individual observers have described these variously as "Ow" or "row" or "hrooa". Actually with this the courtship has already commenced, in which as we have seen both partners take part although playing different rôles. In the second phase, which follows immediately, the behaviour of the male changes. Lorenz speaks of a choking movement. The male ruffles his plumage, especially about the head, but on the whole crouches down as low as possible. The wings are outspread rearward and nearly touch the ground, and in moments of greatest excitement the nictitating membrane is drawn over the eyes, which then suddenly appear quite white. The sounds made also change. The animal utters a comparatively faint and high snuffling note, reproduced by Lorenz as "hruyooyoo". This is the last phase of the courtship play. The behaviour of the male, carried through with the necessary stubbornness, very soon overcomes the female's reluctance, and she takes up the mating attitude.

Matters proceed otherwise among the grey lag-geese. The eager groom here finds himself in a similar position to man. He is not dealing with a single being, but has to intrude into a staid family circle which is defended with dignity by the father. The young gosling must thus admire his chosen one from a distance at first. Should he venture too near her he will be driven off by the father or by both parents. In these animals, strangely enough, the eye already seems to play an important part. The suitor casts some glances full of promise towards his loved one, and it is of decisive importance that she should return these glances if only for a short moment. The play proceeds for some time and the male takes advantage of this time to show his strength and courage in front of the female. He makes an attack on some other bird, to whom he is quite indifferent, with the greatest possible fuss, and finishes the victorious battle with loud cries, the so-called triumphant cry. If the female joins in this noise herself then the engagement seems to be completed and the parents now pronounce their blessing on it.

Amongst ducks all the varieties of courting may be found, between a social wooing which like that of the blackcock takes place even if no females are present, and the courtship for the favours of a particular female. The first extreme is found among mandarin ducks (*Aix galericulata*), the second in wood ducks (*Lampronessa sponsa*). Our most familiar duck, the mallard, behaves somewhat similarly to the mandarin.

It is remarkable that among ducks the females play a very active part. One can distinguish in them two different courting actions, both of which are designed to "make the men mad": the coquettish swimming and the goading or teasing.

The coquettish swim occurs in an early phase. Heinroth has described this very graphically for the mallard. On fine days in late winter, at the end of February, one can often observe at suitable places a round dozen mallard of both sexes in a remarkable social game. At first all is peaceful, but suddenly a female will start to swim to and fro in great haste among the others, her neck outstretched and moving her nictitating membrane in a striking manner. As a reply to this challenging gesture some of the drakes will at once commence a wooing action. The provocative or teasing movements, translated into human values, could be better described as mischief making, and may well start when a pairing arrangement has already been concluded. This instinctive action, which, according to Lorenz, may be seen in nearly all species of ducks, consists in the duck swimming behind her chosen mate and making threatening movements with her head towards other males. Obviously these instinctive actions are calculated to make mischief between her chosen mate and others and increase his passion as much as possible. As we can see in other similar acts, this provocative behaviour among many species has degenerated into an empty ceremonial with, as far as the duck is concerned, the purpose only of shackling the drake to her more firmly.

As already remarked, after the coquettish swim of the females, some of the males, which always go about in groups, begin an ardent dance. These male acts of ardour in the duck species are less remarkable and imposing than those of game birds or birds of paradise, and animal psychologists have taken much trouble to get to the bottom of them. They consist of a multiplicity of movements in sequence and loud utterances of which each perhaps is indistinguishable but which together obviously make a great impression. Lorenz distinguishes the false drinking, the false preening, the waggling, the grunt-whistle, the high-low movement, the up and down motion and the panting. Of all these acts we will deal only with the most important.

When the mallard drakes gather in the spring their gradually increasing excitement is expressed first of all in a characteristic attitude which might well be called their "dominant" or "imposing" attitude. The bird ruffles his head plumage and draws the head down between the shoulders. The body feathers are also slightly ruffled in such a manner that the animal lies as high in the water as possible. Abandoning this attitude he then comes to the actual courtship movements. The most striking of these is the grunt-whistle, already observed by

Heinroth, which in general is caused by the coquettish swimming of a female. It seems that it takes the same form in numerous species.

The grunt-whistle is a characteristic combination of sound and movement. First of all the bird stretches his beak vertically down into the water and erects the forepart of the body steeply out of the water without altering the carriage of the head. The neck then acquires a strong curvature and in this odd position the drake emits a shrill whistle, which is followed by a deep grunting note.

Another wooing act, frequently an answer to the grunt-whistle of some other drake, is the "high-low" movement. The drake first jerks

FIG. 31. Individual pictures from the wooing actions of a mallard drake: (a) coquettish swim of the female; (b) dominant attitude of drake; (c) attitude during the "grunt-whistle"; (d) "short-high" pose; (e) turning of head towards duck by drake.

his head up and back with a loud whistle and at the same time curls his
rump upwards so that the whole bird becomes peculiarly short and
high-looking. The wings also are lifted up and the lovely ornamental
male feathers on the rump can be clearly seen from the side. Altogether
it may well be a case of assuming a position to show off special portions
of the plumage. During these rapidly executed actions the eyes are fixed
upon a particular female. This is the first occasion during this male
display in which a female appears to be the actual object of wooing.
The mated drake always glances modestly at his mate. During the
whole of this social play among the mallard no mating takes place.
The whole thing may well be a matter between the as yet unmated
drakes and ducks of becoming acquainted, which may later lead to
mating. The older couples seem to remain paired for many years, and if
they occasionally separate then they meet again in the autumn in the
same localities and resume their former relationships.

A particularly amiable, one might say chivalrous, behaviour is shown
by the courting male of the American wood duck (*Lampronessa sponsa*).
This is plainly connected with the absence in this species of a social
wooing, and the courtship is always directed towards a particular
female. Here again the female seems to initiate the affair with certain
coquettish movements. But the wooing actions of the males, which in
essence are in the same style as those of the mallard, are somewhat more
impressive. The beautiful dress of the bridegroom is specially well
adapted to act seductively, the proud erection of the splendid hood
enhances the effect and ornamental movements round off the whole.
In this courtship different males usually seek to drive each other away
from the vicinity of the courted one, so that it may even come to
fighting. In this, the courting drake also shows another kind of
behaviour. He suddenly shoots off with great violence in the direction
of the duck, so that one gets the impression that he is about to attack
her furiously with his beak. The duck, which, however, understands
this sign language, is quite unperturbed, and lays her neck flat along the
water, as is done before the mating by a duck who is willing. In the nick
of time the stormy male stops and begins to fondle her by nibbling the
feathers around her head and neck with his beak. These tender displays
are continued after mating.

A whole series of birds has acquired the habit of courting while in
flight, in which every species gives of its best in artistic flying. Particularly beautiful are the mating flights of some birds of prey, such as the

PLATE XI.

Sacred baboon in London Zoo. The leader of the troop in a successful defence against competitors.

PLATES XII AND XIII. Love drama in the life of a lion.

1. Intruder approaches the lovers.

2. The husband (right) advances to do battle.

3. Intruder (left) forced to defend himself.

4. The intruder lies conquered.

PLATE XIV.
Variable tree
mating pos

Position of
of   fresh-
crayfish

kite or the eagle, which describe wonderful circular flights in pairs high in the heavens, suddenly allowing themselves to drop like a plummet, only to rush along and climb again to repeat the performance. This flying in couples is, by the way, only found in some birds of prey. In the remainder the wooing flight is confined to the males. The courting flight of the grey heron is renowned, as he goes through all sorts of aerobatics, describing the most wonderful curves, and is said even to loop the loop. The courtship is then continued on the ground. In addition the lapwing may be given as an example to be observed, especially in the spring, over every water-meadow. At first the bird

Fig. 32. Wooing flight of lapwing. Individual phases from the diving swoop.

flies quite low over the ground, to rise suddenly in a nearly vertical zoom, crying at the same time "Heh heoot" once or twice. The second part of the flight follows immediately, and once again starts in a horizontal flight with another courting note, "whit whit". The most remarkable is, however, the last phase: "With a wild exultant cry the bird swoops down to the depth from on high, turning somersaults or even flying on his back. With this he lets out a loud 'heeoo whit'. He arrests his dive close to the ground and recommences his short flight, also close above the ground as at the beginning. In this last phase of the courting flight, the so-called drumming flight, the lapwing also cuts all sorts of capers, such as flying on his side with one wing-tip up and the other down. In this abnormal flying position a noise audible far and wide is made which has given this flight its name.

"Eventually when the female has squeezed herself into a slight depression in the ground the male will dive down near her and alight, but does not by any means go straight to her; he only ogles her in a curious manner, executes a little tripping run to right and to left, with short pauses, before standing still and making movements indistinguishable from deep bows. Now the female stirs, raises herself a little on her heels, rocks backwards and forwards dipping her tail gently and utters a *sotto voce* very unpleasant-sounding croaking babble with which she seems to encourage the male. He now comes nearer and expresses his warm feelings by running forward a few steps, stopping and seizing a grass stem or suchlike object in his beak and casting it over his shoulder behind him. . . . Does the male hint by this at nest-building to induce favourable feelings in the female? I can hardly believe it, however necessary nest-building may be." (After Liebe.)

Amongst the most select masters of flight of this kind are the snipe, which are often to be found in the same localities as the lapwing. The small jack snipe (*Limnocryptes minimus*) combines his show flight with a somewhat monotonous wooing call. In the snipe (*Capella gallinago*) the wooing call has disappeared, but not the production of noises. The animal creates a peculiar bleating sound when he shoots like a diving aeroplane from the heights which has earned him the name "heavenly he-goat". The sound is said to be caused by the vibration of the outer specially formed tail feathers.

In humming-birds the splendour of their plumage combines with the astounding flying skill of the male. They are particularly well adapted to these masterly performances, since they work their wings differently to other birds. Their wing beats follow each other with unbelievable speed, sixty to seventy times a second, and make possible a very swift and dartingly tortuous flight. A recent observer of these enchanting little birds describes their courting flight in the following words: "With vibrating wings he describes curve after curve, like a pendulum, back and forth, to and fro, up and down. More and more impassioned does this soundless love song become, higher, ever higher, swings the curve . . . suddenly the bird sweeps straight up for sixty feet or more. For a moment he hovers overhead then dives in a spectacular swoop to earth, brakes suddenly in midfall at the level of the tiny little female's head. She sits on a twig and watches. There he pauses on whirring wings and she sees him glitter like a flaming jewel."

We experience a lively disappointment with the songsters. Whoever has not made a special study of these things will certainly imagine that song is the most important factor in their wooing. This fits nicely into our own ideas. It reminds us of serenades by the lover to his dear one, and of the glorious era of the knights errant, of minstrels roving from castle to castle and of their noble singing contests, giving of their best in song.

But the harsh truth is quite otherwise. The singing of our song-birds is closely related to the concept of territory. Each male song-bird sings only in this, his own proper territory, and instantly becomes silent if he enters a neighbour's region by chance. When he bursts into song with a fervour which makes us think that the greatest luck or deepest yearning causes the songster's little breast to swell to bursting point, it turns out that all it means is a warning to all listeners, "Here I be". The song is a threat to all other males, to whom entrance into his preserve is forbidden. It has nothing to do with love except in so far as this notice to males to keep out is also an enticement to marriage-hungry females to penetrate into his preserve.

The agreement between the partners for mating seems, amongst the songsters, to come about in the simplest possible manner, so that one can hardly talk of a courtship. Something has already been said of the yellow bunting. Without doubt the female does the choosing. She roams about and has the freedom of all the territories. It is, however, by no means proved that the handsomer or more vocal male enjoys an advantage.

Since, of the song-birds, only the yellow bunting and the robin have been studied, it is certain that further observations will disclose much that is new. In many song-birds it is said that during a certain phase the males violently pursue the females. By contrast, it is precisely in these creatures that coquettish actions on the part of the females may often be observed.

Courtship amongst mammals

A true wooing comparable with that of the birds is a great rarity in mammals. Certainly it must be admitted that we have very little information even for the most common of our animals. A process which can relatively often be observed is the pursuit or drive (see Plate VII).

The pursuit of the doe by the roebuck has indeed been well known since ancient times, and has very often been depicted by artists. It probably ends, as it does with the ass, in a true overpowering. It seems to be characteristic that it is chiefly quite young ones, that have no close experience with a buck, which resign themselves to such a chase. They are said to utter a characteristic note during it, which is interpreted as a cry of fear. Experienced does, so it is said, do not flee from the buck. The roebuck is, as is known, attracted by the whistle of the does. Hunters make use of this by imitating the sound. In hares things happen fairly temperamentally and the poor doe must often lose plenty of fur. In contrast to the deer, there is, in general, no prolonged chase over long distances, since the jinking female hare is able to evade her pursuer in a more confined space.

Rabbits, it seems, behave more chivalrously, as do also squirrels, among which some pursuing is, however, also done; in between, true courting games are also played. In rabbits the game also begins with some chasing. The male chases the female round, who is either unwilling or at least acts as if she were. She occasionally jinks so that the male rushes past her, but for the rest he keeps control. The game is frequently interrupted by a common search for food. The second phase is the showing of the scut, and this may be compared most readily to a bird-wooing. The male goes about on raised hind legs and carries his tail laid along the back, thus exposing the white underside, the scut. At the same time he goes through various manœuvres known as the false withdrawal and the parade. In the former the male walks away stiff-legged to a distance of about two yards from the female, who sits still, continuously showing her scut. This may be repeated several times. In the parade the male circles the female quite closely within a radius of two and a half feet, continuing to show his scut. The movements are mostly slow, but may change to a stiff-legged gallop.

A somewhat remarkable accompanying phenomenon is that usually during the scut-showing the male occasionally urinates on the female. We must not forget that mammals are scent animals. Probably this action has a powerful aphrodisiac effect on the female. Mating, for the rest, seems to occur at night or perhaps in the burrow. During the day the females always refuse the male.

In squirrels also the mating game commences with a pursuit of the female, which may, according to her temperament, develop hotly or quietly. With each approach to the female the male gives a peculiar call, which may be reproduced as "moock moock". He is supposed to imitate the cry of the young animals, and perhaps it has the effect of restraining the aggressive spirit of the female. The running away of the female throughout is only a ruse. She runs a couple of steps and then stops with uplifted tail. Occasionally the female tries to attract the male's attention. Such a coquettish attitude has also been described for the female hare. Throughout, both partners show a particular way of running which is called the "dominant run". The run is carried out jerkily in this case, and the animals create a variety of sounds together.

They clash their teeth and simultaneously beat with their paws violently on the ground. When this prelude has lasted some time the courtship approaches its climax, and this is distinguished by a quite special and characteristic wooing position in the male. He places himself transversely in front of the female and executes various movements with his tail, which he first waves to and fro horizontally, then making a wider sweeping motion and finally placing it quite slowly along his back. In this pose the animal remains motionless for up to a minute. The whole courtship may last some hours until the mating finally results.

Schenkel has contributed a very important study on the behaviour of captive wolves in the Zoological Gardens at Basle, but it is self-evident that the findings cannot with certainty be applied to free animals.

When a number of wolves are brought together under constraint, and thereby artificially converted into a pack, first of all and in both sexes a social ranking is established by fighting, threatening gestures, intimidation and other methods. When this is accomplished there are two head beasts or leaders, a dog and a bitch. These two form a pair, the only one in this artificial pack. It can be seen that anything in the nature of a courtship simply does not take place. The two animals are not drawn together by any erotic ties but by their social position in the community.

If this pairing does not occur exactly at the mating season the relations between the two are at first only formal. It has been established that between the two no question of precedence or quarrelling arises. As a prelude to later mating occasional snuffling round the neck, at the sides of the head and nose may be noted, although the same may occur between dog wolves also. At the actual rutting season other things become more important. In an extreme macrosmatic animal such as a wolf, it is understandable that the smell of a she-wolf on heat assumes the very greatest importance for the he-wolf. Obviously the she-wolf knows this instinctively, for the presentation of the anal region by raising the tail occurs, an action which at other times may also be observed among the males. In them, however, it has naturally not a sexual but a social meaning. The leader she-wolf paces about with raised tail in a mincing dance step and affectionately "whining" or "singing" in front of her mate. The ardent male leader wolf answers this very clear demonstration by smelling and licking her genital regions, a course of action which is permitted to no other wolf in the pack.

As an expression of her erotic mood the she-wolf carries out various coquettish actions, affectionate squeezing and rubbing, in certain circumstances also mounting, an act which may be also observed in other mammals.

(c) THE PHYSIOLOGICAL PREREQUISITES FOR MATING

The desire of the male has, in spite of all the wooing, naturally only a meaning when the female is in a physiological condition which allows of mating. Our most precise knowledge on this is from the vertebrates, and we will here confine ourselves to the mammals, which possess a strictly regulated, rhythmically progressing sexual cycle. In most wild species which have only a short yearly mating season these matters arrange themselves, in any case, of their own accord, for outside the rutting season the males do not bother about the females. Besides these monoestrous species, there are numerous polyoestrous animals, particularly in the tropics, which to a varying degree have many periods of heat during the year. To these also belong our domestic animals, which under the influence of domestication have become polyoestrous. Among the mammals only the apes are ready for mating during the entire cycle. In horses, in which the cycle lasts nineteen to twenty-two days, such readiness continues for only four and a quarter to nine days; in pigs, in spite of a cycle of equal duration, only two days; in cows, only a matter of thirteen to fourteen hours.

It is noteworthy that in recent studies similar conditions have been found in some insects. When the female of the grasshopper (*Euthystira brachyptera*) has carried out her last moult the eggs are still undeveloped. The first egg-laying only takes place eight days later, and then is repeated rhythmically at certain time intervals. Since there are six oviducts in the ovary, six eggs are laid each time. The fertilized eggs leave the ovary one to two days before the egg-laying and reach the outlet passages, where they next lie. The female grasshopper varies her behaviour towards the ardent male according to the differing condition of her internal organs. Thus freshly hatched females, which have no mature eggs, ward off the male for a couple of days. Following this is a period of active preparedness which also lasts a few days. As soon as the movement of the mature eggs into the oviduct sets in, readiness to mate again gives way to defence.

8

SEXUAL FIGHTS OF ANIMALS

(a) THE FIGHTS OF MAMMALS

UNDER the heading of sexual fights are included the various acts of aggression which male animals of a species perpetrate against each other. One thing all these battles have in common is that the victor is in a position adequately to satisfy his sexual urge. Matters vary very much in detail, however, in different cases, so that one is tempted to try classifying these sexual contests. There are fights by challenge, fights for access and competitive fights. We will examine a typical example of each.

The classical example of a challenging battle has for long been the rutting battle of our red deer. The rutting call of the stag is a real experience for every townsman who for the first time hears the primitive power of the sound. It serves as a challenge to an opponent whom he does not even know yet and has never seen (see Plate VII). Here also we must again remember that we are dealing with an instinct. The stag does not call because he wants to challenge another, but because he must; because the state of inner agitation in which he finds himself compels him to call. The details of this action are very little known. When all is quiet in the reserve and no beasts of prey are about to disturb the deer, all the stags call at the right time; the hinds remain quietly nearby without showing any special excitement.

If at this time two stags approach near to each other it may come to a fight. Moreover the fight is short and sharp. When an old, experienced leader whilst driving his herd before him hears a rival calling to one side, he will instantly attack him and the clashing of their antlers is soon heard.

If the other is a weaker beast our stag soon returns to his hinds, whilst the vanquished one disappears in the bushes bent on some new adventure. If two equally powerful stags encounter each other the battle is of course fiercer. Nature has, however, taken care that these fights do not become too murderous. The wide spread of the antlers is, for another stag, anything but a dangerous weapon. The two beasts stand face to face and charge each other's antlers so that these mostly suffer the impact. It will seldom be possible for the stag to inflict a serious wound on his opponent with one of the dagger-like projecting tines of his antlers. Nevertheless there are tragic exceptions. In the reserves guarded by man so-called "murderers" are found now and then. Amongst these are included those older stags which have not got branched antlers like a ten or eighteen pointer, but who have remained at the stage of a brocket which has on each side only one long un-branched horn; such a simplified prong acting like a spear is a very much more dangerous weapon for an opponent than the normal antlers. These murderers must be quickly shot, before they can do much damage.

Another tragic occurrence is the occasional fight to a finish between two well-matched stags. It may happen that they entangle their many-pointed antlers in such a manner that they cannot clear them, and a dreadful fate lies ahead of them if man does not come to the rescue. They finally become weary, fall down and come to a miserable end. In some museums the heads of a couple of such stags which perished in this way are exhibited. In Nature wolves would have put an end to them, for the poor beasts are quite helpless.

The fight for access is seen in a particularly instructive manner in the fur seal (*Arctocephalus ursinus*). The social community life of these peculiar beasts will be described elsewhere. There we shall see that the males can be separated into two categories, the full adults, each of which has gathered a harem round him, and the younger males, which are not yet allowed to approach by the elders and which must content them-selves with a nearby stretch of ground and no harem. Now and again, however, an urge to reproduce awakens in one or another of these young males, and the question arises as to how these males assert their right. Here also there is but one way, to fight. The youngster who feels himself strong enough to come to grips with one of the older colossi ventures outside the bachelor beach into the lines of the grown-ups and starts a quarrel with one of the old bulls. Whether at this point any choice is exercised we do not know, yet it seems quite possible that the youths can distinguish between bulls in the full flower of their maturity and those which are already on the decline, and that it is precisely one of these, which promises results, that they go for. These fights are by no means harmless. Seals as fish-eaters have a formidable dentition with many sharp teeth. The opponents seek to seize each other with these so that soon much blood flows. The weaker must eventually give in. Now his destiny fulfils itself. So far the other males have stood aside as interested but neutral spectators. But as soon as the issue has been decided they all fall upon the vanquished. If the old beast was incapable of withstanding the youthful strength of his rival, he must now, assailed on all sides by bites, take to his heels without delay and live a lonely and joyless life apart from the main herd—alas, without a harem.

This kind of battle, which we may also call a separation fight, may well be the most frequent one amongst communal mammals like cattle, antelopes, deer, wild horses, other herd animals or apes (see Plate XI). Its start seems to be assured by instinct, and biologically has the effect of removing from the community senile individuals which could endanger the continuance or welfare of the whole herd. If we choose the African Cape buffalo as an example, then the leading bull is continually exposed to the danger of being displaced by a younger rival, and in the rutting season fights must occur over and over again in which the leader must prove his mettle and mastery. The end of the story is, however, always the same; the old one must one day give way to a younger rival, and as is the case with the fur seal, he must become a morose hermit. Nevertheless these hermits may certainly join together in troops. We may also conclude with certainty that these fights take place amongst wild horses. Obviously they have never been observed, but since we know that domestic horses have changed their instincts hardly at all it is most interesting to listen to the arresting story of such a battle between two domestic stallions told by Antonius in 1937. After the two animals have circled each other several times in a threatening manner in which the head is held quite low (see also p. 144), they charge each other, throwing up their heads, attempting to seize each other's throats and to throw each other. In the case observed, one stallion succeeded in seizing the other by the throat, whereupon both horses reared up. Although the attacked one was able to free himself, he had obviously had enough. On the whole we can conclude from this and other observations that in horses the attack is carried out with the teeth and the defence with the hooves.

In any case, a fight between two stallions is not a particularly nice sight, and is really very different to the phantasies usually painted by our artists. It shows, however, that in this most tamed of all our domestic animals a residue of unimaginable savagery is concealed.

Of the sexual fights of solitarily living animals which visit a female only during the mating time and live with her for a brief period, very little is known. If a third party crosses the path of these two this also may lead to a struggle, in this case for the possession of a single female.

Such fights have probably been observed most frequently in hares, but in these no blood flows. As Diezel writes in his *Coursing* (1849). "The chief strain in the character of the hare is fear and shyness, wherefor without doubt 'Father' Linnæus conferred on him the nickname of timidus, that is, the fearful. Faint-hearted souls love peace, hence concord is natural to them. Only when the sexual urge moves them can one frequently see them in conflict. In these duels which are started by jealousy no one loses his life, since they resemble the petty feuds of exasperated fishwives, who injure each other only with their nails and thus only a tuft of hair or at most a handful is torn off, so here a few tufts of wool fly and with that the matter ends."

Less good-natured is the strife amongst lions (see Plates XII and XIII). Strictly speaking the lions do not belong to this section, since they live in families. In his youth, however, the male must probably commence with a monogamous mating and thus far we may include him amongst the types described above. A peculiar accident last year brought such a love drama from the life of a lion into the field of view of a photographer's camera. In the first picture we see the couple sitting peacefully together, then an intruder approaches threateningly. Instantly the rightful husband rises and goes to meet the unwelcome rival, growling. Of the resulting combat only a few momentary still photographs are reproduced. In the third picture we see that the intruder is very soon forced to defend himself, and in the fourth finally that, struck by heavy blows of the paws, he lies on the ground whilst the avenger stands in front of him in a fierce attitude, ready to make an end of him. This is the first and only time that such a sexual battle has been observed closely and photographs of it secured. We do not know how far we are justified in coming to conclusions from this single case about other such fights among mammals living solitarily, but it is tempting to do so, for in all other vertebrates from birds to fish we meet the basic law that, in all sexual fights, it is not brute force but right which prevails, and the intruder into the harmony of marital coexistence is heavily punished, as we have just seen with the lion.

We have here the astonishing fact that amongst animals matters are considerably more moral than amongst humans. In the higher social strata of Europeans the duel was formerly the order of the day. How often then did it happen that the protector of his marital rights lay fatally wounded, whilst the frivolous fortune-hunter triumphed merely because he could handle a weapon more skilfully than his opponent.

The riddle of how it comes about that in man the immoral so often wins and in beasts the moral is easy to solve. Man acts from cold-blooded reflection, the animal from passion. Crimes of passion have certainly been brought into disrepute among civilized men, yet it is still very doubtful whether this denial of justice always functions. The philosopher Nietzsche once discussed the question with an English philosopher and then wrote down the indignant words: "To forbid acts of affection means to forbid decent acts altogether". The normal sensitive man and also the normal animal gets furious if he feels he has been unjustly treated, be it that he is being attacked or that he is threatened in some vital right. Here naturally mistakes may occur, but usually the situation is probably unequivocal. Behind the considered act of an intelligent man there can be a plan of satanic iniquity, in a capacity for which man excels the animals by far. To recapitulate: in sexual combats of the vertebrates affection increases the strength of the attacked many times, and thus it comes about that right always wins.

(b) THE FIGHTS OF BIRDS

The victory of right shows itself most clearly in fish and birds. Research into animal psychology has drawn attention to the great importance of one particular factor in many animals, namely the possession of a territory. At the beginning of the mating season each adult male seeks out a fixed site, and the neighbouring region becomes his property or his territory in that he will not allow any other animal into it. This law is so for quite different groups of animals, that is to say for insects (dragon-flies), fishes, mammals and birds. The fight between two males in this case is not for the possession of a female but for the territory. For this some very remarkable rules of play hold good, which are in complete agreement with those we have just enunciated. It is not the stranger who wins, but the rightful owner of the preserve. David Lack in his charming study of the robin has supported this fact by a pretty experiment. He placed a male robin, in his own proper territory, in a closed cage. As a known quarrelsome male from the neighbouring preserve flew by, the bird in the cage immediately took up his dominant attitude and flung towards the intruder an energetic challenging song, although he could not leave the cage. The other hastily retreated to his own preserve. Now the cage was moved to the neighbouring region in which the previous intruder was boss. No sooner was the latter aware of the other than he attacked the cage with great fury, whilst the captive, who just before had shown himself so combative, now made himself as small as possible and showed no sign of fight. From this we may infer that each male respects the territory of the others, but defends his own with the greatest bitterness. This is an astonishingly complicated process, and to examine it more closely would repay even a philosopher. Among the strong-flying birds it would nevertheless be wrong, therefore, to conclude that each bird is to a certain extent imprisoned in his own territory. He can range far afield to find food and thus penetrate into other birds' preserves. If the owner does not show up then all is well. Should he, however, prepare for battle then the intruder clears out swiftly. Naturally it may also come to a fight between the owner of a preserve and another who as yet has no preserve. By our now well-known rules of the game the victory always goes to the former.

Serious fights which are sometimes a matter of life and death occur chiefly among the unmated fowls. The best known is the domestic cock. Anyone who has lived for some time in the country must have seen from time to time two cocks with ruffled feathers confronting each other and then suddenly going for each other so that the feathers fly. It is well known, for instance, that even today, say in Indonesia, cock-fighting in which large sums are wagered is one of the favourite amusements of the people. Just as in Spain fighting bulls are bred, so in Indonesia especially combative races of fowls are cultivated. The danger of the fight, which does not affect spectators, is also increased by giving the birds steel spurs with which they hack each other about most frightfully. This combativeness in fowls is by no means bred into them by man as a result of domestication; it is also found in wild birds. The German naturalist Doflein observed such courting fights in Ceylon among jungle fowl (*Gallus stanleyi*) and writes that here also one of the combatants now and then does not leave the field alive. The hens watch from a distance.

Such fights are, however, not always so sanguinary. Even among these polygamous birds the fight frequently develops into a tourney without any bloodshed, during which the female spectators here also become attracted by one or the other. The most frequently observed and described of these struggles are probably those of our own black-cocks. We owe an outstanding description of one, from the Dachau marshland, to Doflein: "In the grey dawn the cock made his appearance near our hide with a peculiar hissing noise—chouh-ee. After having remained absolutely still for nearly ten minutes on the ground where he alighted, to assure himself that all was safe, he commenced his dance. Whilst bowing and hopping about he gave tongue to his grumbling and shushing, made similar motions to the grouse, his hopping became quite bizarre and frantic as more and more cocks joined in with their hissing cries of chouh-ee, chouh-ee, occasionally alighting on our shelter on their first arrival. By this time all the cocks were bowing, revolving and skipping like mad. At times one would jump vertically half a yard or more. Suddenly two flew at each other, attacking with beak and claw. Feathers flew and one of them left the scene, vanquished, to seek another court and try his luck again. Others went in to the attack, hissed and spat at each other, ran hither and thither and in fact conducted a mock battle in pantomime. So it went on for hours, from four in the morning until going on for eight. Meanwhile lots of hens, uttering a soft cackling noise, had gathered nearby."

The purely ceremonial and social combat of the ruffs has already been fully described.

(c) THE FIGHTS OF REPTILES

Amongst the reptiles rutting fights have been described in many groups: crocodiles, tortoises, lizards and snakes. In some tropical forms matters seem to proceed somewhat temperamentally, but here we will limit ourselves to species nearer home, which have rather tamer customs.

In our lizards, for instance the wall lizard, the fighting is not really to be taken seriously; it is fought to strict rules. It starts by the opponents taking up positions facing each other and in an attitude of stiffest "dominant" bearing, whereupon one male will bite the other on the nape of the neck (see Plate X). We should expect that the victim would now defend himself, but these lizards manage things according to Nietzsche's immortal words: "Not to react, this also is a form of strength". The biter remains unmoved in his dominant attitude; at most he will make a defensive movement with his hind leg. When the biter has let go then comes the other's turn and the exchange of bites now continues bite for bite. At last one of them abandons the struggle, drops his dominant demeanour and flees. The defeat has a very lasting effect. Immediately after the fight the vanquished male flees from all others and even cowers before a weaker one which normally he would dominate. It is only gradually that his spirit regains its poise.

Snake fights have been described as pretty lukewarm affairs. Among common vipers it has been observed at mating time that the rival males raise the fore-part of their bodies and mutually attempt to entwine the other; they also bump heads. Never, however, do they bite. These remarkable games of movement have also been classed as courting dances. Since, however, this concerns the behaviour of one male towards another it seems more fitting to include it here (see Plate X).

(d) FIGHTING AMONG FISH

Actual courtship contests are never seen amongst amphibians. They are, however, frequent among fishes, particularly amongst those species which take possession of a territory during the mating season and defend it against all comers. Such a fight, the object of which on one side is to drive off an intruder, and on the other to conquer a territory, must of course be regarded as a fight between rivals.

These combats proceed exactly as in lizards by set rules. Below we will examine somewhat more fully the methods of fighting employed by the males of a fish known as *Hemichromis*. If during the mating season two sexually mature and more or less equally matched males are brought together, the first thing that happens is that both go into full display and take up a dominant attitude. The black pigmentation distributed over the whole body vanishes in a matter of seconds and at once the entire ventral side of the head, breast and the fore-part of the belly turns scarlet. Furthermore, the fins are spread so that the fish looks truly magnificent. Now, certain manœuvres are carried out. Both fish swim in such a manner that they keep station broadside to broadside and head to tail of each other. In this position they exchange powerful blows of their tails which strike the other over the head. These tail-beatings may be repeated several times, interrupted by a swimming stroke or two. The main battle develops, however, from a different position, in which the creatures face each other head to head and in which the gill covers, which are decorated with a gold-circled spot, become the show pieces. The climax of the fight is the "mouth biting". Each fish seizes the other's lips with his jaws, and they drag each other hither and thither. What this exceedingly odd mode of fighting means is not fully understood. Dangerous wounds can certainly not be inflicted in this way. Probably, however, a sort of exhaustion supervenes and, to put it briefly, one of the combatants gives in and departs.

Among sticklebacks the fights which may frequently be observed clearly have the character of territorial battles. Each male during the spawning season chooses a small area in which he builds a nest and declares it his private property. The combativeness of the owner towards other sticklebacks varies. At its most intense other male

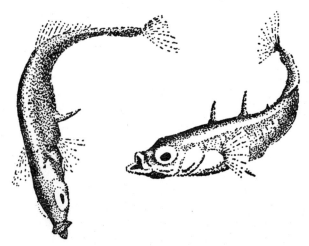

FIG. 33. Male sticklebacks fighting.

sticklebacks which are also ready to spawn and which show this by the red colour of their bellies are attacked. The opposition to other males which are not ready to spawn and to females is weaker. Gravid females are never attacked. As has been clearly shown by the use of experimental decoys, the red colouring plays the major part in setting off this impulse. Nevertheless, it has been determined that red dummies are not fought with the same energy as living rivals. Other things must therefore also play a part. It is doubtful whether the colouring of the eyes has any significance. It cannot be denied, however, that it has a significance for the threatening movement with which every combat is preceded. This consists in the threatening animal showing his opponent a flank, in the course of which he takes up a nearly vertical attitude, and erecting his pectoral spine, which is directed away from the body (see Fig 33, left) and towards his opponent.

In sticklebacks it is particularly evident that strength is not the decisive factor for victory. According to Wunder, the victor in the battle "is he which is the older inhabitant over the one that is the newer inhabitant, the male with the nest over the one without, the male that is more careful about his nest over that one that neglects his, the male with eggs in his nest over him without eggs".

(e) THE SUBMISSIVE ATTITUDE

In many vertebrates a fight is brought to an end when the vanquished surrenders and also assumes an attitude which makes the conqueror clearly aware of it. Animal psychologists call this a submissive attitude. It is of importance that amongst all animals living in communities the meaning of such a sexual combat is never that one of the opponents is killed, only that he gives up his place to the other. The submissive attitude is thus a link in a complicated sign language by which animals of the same species can come to a close understanding. The characteristic of this attitude is that the beaten animal assumes such a position that it would be very easy for his opponent to dispatch him. In certain respects this ceremony may be compared to the behaviour of soldiers who give themselves up, who throw away their weapons and raise their arms. As Lorenz says, more succinctly, "the suppliant offers the most vulnerable portion of his body". Since, however, the battle is fought under certain rules, the conqueror is simply not in a position to take advantage of this offer and to give his opponent the *coup de grâce*. All that remains for him to do is to stop the fight.

(f) SEXUAL BATTLES OF INVERTEBRATES

Even among the invertebrates sexual fights are not entirely unknown. Probably they are much more frequent than we at present know. They seem, however, to occur only in arthropods. Such fights, which are most certainly between rivals, have been recorded for some crabs (*Carcinus, Gelasimus, Callinectes*), but no fundamental study has yet been undertaken. Nearer home, stag beetles have been observed by competent entomologists to nip each other vigorously with their large pincers. That one of them may lose his life in these exchanges is at any rate not impossible (see Plate X).

The best known are the fights between male crickets, because in Italy and elsewhere there is a very ancient and popular custom of keeping these creatures in small cages and of releasing them to fight each other. Such contests may be seen at annual fairs and similar events. The cricket battle there has, however, been arranged artificially. When the insects are free such a thing is presumably a rarity, for in the fields each male cricket lives in his own hole and each has his own preserve. "In a chance meeting or one brought about on purpose, after a short shrinking away they at once start to feel each other all over with their antennæ. On this follow immediately the 'rival' calls. As a rule the 'owning' animal begins before the one intruding into his realm. In a normal contest the intruder at once replies with a rival's call. After a few shrill, irregularly spaced, short rival calls, both will spring at each other with wide-open mandibles. The further course of the fight may vary. Either the opponents grip each other firmly, when the weaker may be hauled along a short way by the stronger until he can free himself and take to his heels, or both flinch back a little after the initial leap, renew the excited rival calls and again leap upon each other. This leaping and hesitating may be repeated a couple of times until one or the other submits and seeks the wide open spaces." (Zipelius, 1949.)

9

THE UNION

IN the preceding pages we have discussed all that goes before the two sexes unite, and we now approach the problem of the union itself. We must not forget, however, that the core of the problem is not the union of the sexual partners but the combination of ovum and sperm. We must therefore return to this problem, which was dealt with at the beginning: either the ovum is fertilized outside the body or else this process takes place inside the female organism. In the first case we speak of an external fertilization, in the second of an internal one.

The division into the two kinds of fertilization is very remarkable. At first it may seem obvious that external fertilization, with the exception of some animals which are dying out, should be limited to aquatic animals, since the delicate sperms would instantly dry up on land. On the other hand it is by no means all aquatic animals that make use of this simplest of all ways of fertilization. In the lower worms there are already numerous groups in which, although they live in water, a true mating and internal fertilization can nevertheless be observed, for instance in the threadworms. On the other hand, external fertilization can be seen in even the highest animals, even in vertebrates, as in fish and amphibians.

It is not very easy to understand the logic underlying these two kinds of fertilization, but there is one definite correlation and that is in the number of eggs deposited. All aquatic animals having an external fertilization produce an immense number of eggs. In the sea-urchin the mature ovaries, looking like yellow grapes, fill a large proportion of the body cavity and the number of eggs probably runs to a hundred thousand. In fish, where the ovary also fills the entire body cavity, the number may be several millions. The high number is necessary because in external fertilization the eggs float about, a defenceless prey to all their enemies, and only a very few survive to develop into adult animals; by far the greater number are destroyed. In those animals in which internal fertilization takes place the number is always much smaller. This is made possible because these eggs mostly enjoy some sort of protection. Either they remain in the mother's body during early development, or if they are expelled as spawn they are protected by shells or by some other arrangement, frequently also by the mother watching over them. Nature thus has a choice of two courses in aquatic creatures, both leading to the same goal, and she follows sometimes the one, sometimes the other.

It can be shown quite clearly that external fertilization, in which both ova and spermatozoa are simply emptied into the water, is found chiefly in marine animals. The sea as the mother of all life is infinitely more suitable than fresh water to the existence of delicate larvæ, and for the development of suspended eggs.

If now we examine external fertilization a little more closely, we shall find that there is no relation between the kind of fertilization and the level of organization of the animal, and this must be emphasized.

(a) EXTERNAL FERTILIZATION

The process of external fertilization has indeed been known for ages. It has, however, not been investigated in detail. When eggs and milt are extruded into the water the mobile sperms must seek the eggs. It is self-evident that this is only possible when the two animals are close together, so that the sperms have only a comparatively short distance to cover. The "close together" can be brought about in two different ways, either because from the first the animals remain side by side even outside the breeding period, or because they seek each other when that time comes.

Let us examine the first. If you stand on the rocky shore of a clear sea like the Mediterranean and look into shallow water, you may see here and there small sea-urchins that have bored a little into the rocks. Having found the first one, the eye becomes accommodated, and you then see that there is a veritable colony of sea-urchins. They live on every rock, usually barely a yard apart, and there may be many hundreds together in a very restricted space. A large number of sea creatures behave in the same way, for example the acorn barnacles (Balanidæ), small fixed crustacea, which on many coasts settle on every stone and every wooden post in their thousands. On open sands the same phenomenon may be seen. The lugworm (*Arenicola marina*) shows, by the heaps of sand it throws up, that it inhabits the entire shore of certain coastal sand flats in countless numbers, one beside the other.

In these circumstances only one problem remains for their propagation, and that is the time. Care must be taken that both male and female cast their germ cells into the water simultaneously, so that these may quickly meet. How this happens we know to the smallest degree only by actual observation. In some sea-urchins, chitons, whelks and other marine creatures it has been shown that during the mild spring-time, when the buds are bursting, any animal in which the reproductive glands are quite full will begin discharging germ cells into the water. From this animal a quite faint scent must emanate and communicate itself to the neighbouring creatures. This acts as a signal, for now all or most of the others follow the example of the first and each sends a whole cloud of sperms or ova into the water.

A singular problem, one which has usually been somewhat disregarded even in strictly scientific books, is presented by the scarcer species. Every naturalist or collector knows that in all classes of animals there are, besides the quite common species which may be gathered in hundreds, rare species which are found only now and then in the sea, during collecting or fishing or in a plankton net. When these live on the sea bottom they may be separated from each other by many yards, perhaps miles. How then is it possible for the individual to give a signal to another and how can the sperms reach the ova? We will not, however, pursue this knotty problem any farther.

Similar difficulties arise for the inhabitants of fast-flowing waters such as mountain streams. Actually one would expect that in all such animals one would find an internal fertilization, since with external fertilization there is the danger of the sperms being washed away instantly.

The second case, in which the animals seek each other out before discharging their eggs and milt into the water, is found chiefly in fish and amphibians. It is almost certainly widespread also among the lower animals, but our knowledge on this is still very imperfect. Thus some marine bristle-worms, which for the rest of the year lead a very secluded life in some crevice or burrow at the bottom of the sea, in the spring suddenly betake themselves into open waters. A good example is seen in the largest of the polychætes (*Nereis virens*), which can be seen swimming about, in Kiel harbour for instance, in the evenings during the month of March. There is scarcely any doubt that these animals are on the look-out for mates.

Many observations have been made with regard to fishes. In suitably arranged large aquaria, in spring, plaice can be seen swimming about in couples, alongside each other for long periods, until finally both simultaneously discharge clouds of eggs and sperms into the water. It is in this kind of way that fertilization is best achieved. Many fishes which lay their eggs at random on the bottom, such as salmon, first search for a suitable spawning-place and then make a trough with their snouts. In this the eggs are laid and then sprinkled with semen by the male.

In the blind urge of their desire fishes do exactly the same as the research worker who carries out an artificial insemination of such eggs.

Matters become more complicated when a proper nest is made for the reception of the eggs. We will return to this in the chapter on the care of the offspring. The behaviour of frogs and toads is too well known to need further discussion. The male who clamps himself to the back of the usually larger female will in certain circumstances wait patiently for days until his time comes. As soon as the female allows the eggs to emerge, they are sprayed with semen.

External fertilization is connected by several transitions with internal fertilization to such an extent that in fact it is often difficult to say where an individual case should be placed. It very often happens that only the sperms are set free into the water, whilst the ova remain in the mother's body. Here, however, it is always that the eggs have already left the uterus and are stored in some outer cavities in the female's body. This distinguishes the examples to be discussed from true internal fertilization. The process is usually recognized by the young being born alive. In the lowest metazoa this is quite a frequent phenomenon. Thus most sponges are viviparous, for one finds, at the appropriate time, not only eggs but also larvæ in all stages of development embedded in their tissues. The spermatozoa obviously enter through the numerous pores in its skin, through which a sponge takes nourishment into the canal system within its body. Thence they find their way to the ova scattered throughout the tissues.

It is the same with the Cœlenterates. If in summer you fish a few jellyfish (*Aurelia aurita*) from the water you can see that in some the four large mouth tentacles are coloured yellow. Those who are less well acquainted with natural phenomena may explain this appearance, familiar to those living on the coast, by saying that these arms continue their existence as starfish as soon as they sink to the bottom. Unfortunately, instead of this romantic explanation we have to offer a simpler one. These yellowish tentacles are covered with planula larvæ which cling there in their thousands. Probably the eggs, which in these animals protrude into the water, have been fertilized already in the ovary by sperms floating in the water, the developing larvæ then clinging to the mouth tentacles.

There are also viviparous sea-anemones, such as the pretty little *Actinia equina*, vividly red, frequently met with on rocky coasts. In midsummer one finds many of them with the hollow body cavity filled with perfect little sea-anemones, which shortly after are ejected through the mouth by the female parent and forthwith begin their independent life. Since the body cavity, usually called the gastral cavity, serves chiefly for the digestion of captured prey, we have here the remarkable performance of a mother storing her offspring to a certain extent in her own stomach. At this point the important question is, in what manner does the fertilization of the eggs take place? In sea-anemones the eggs originate on the so-called septa which subdivide the gastral cavity. When mature they fall into that cavity. The sperms are presumably carried in by the pulsation of the gullet.

Turning for a moment to the higher animals, we find a similar state of affairs in fresh-water molluscs. Here again precise observations have not been made and we must be content to draw our conclusions from what we ourselves see. The fresh-water mussels belonging to the genera *Anodonta* and *Unio* each have two large gills to the right and left, which are almost as long as the whole body. In late summer these gills are very swollen, and their inner cavity is filled with hundreds of thousands of tiny larvæ which later become free and are dispersed in the water. Here again the process must be that the male mussels empty their milt into the water and the females draw this water through the gill cavity, where the fertilization of the eggs which have been expelled from their ovaries takes place.

Lastly we will choose an example from among the crustacea. On the shore one may often find all the rocks and wooden piles standing in water closely occupied by barnacles (*Balanus*). They are hermaphrodite and each possesses an extraordinarily long penis. In the breeding season they extend this as far as possible and spray their neighbours with the seminal fluid, like a gardener watering his flowers. *Balanus* feeds by sucking in the surrounding water with all it contains. The spermatozoa naturally also find their way into the spacious cavity of the shell on occasion, and there meet the ova which have been extruded into the same cavity.

(b) INTERNAL FERTILIZATION

Fertilization by means of spermatophores

By spermatophores is understood seed packets containing a large mass of spermatozoa covered outwardly with an envelope. The advantages accruing from these peculiar structures are twofold. First a large number of spermatozoa can be transferred in each; secondly, the protective covering makes it possible even for land animals to

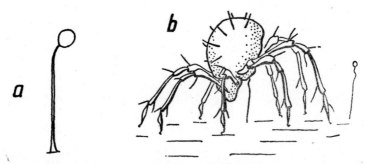

Fig. 34. Simple spermatophores: (*a*) *Orchesella villosa* (primitive insect)—natural scale length of stalk $\frac{1}{100}$th of an inch; (*b*) moss mite (Belba) at the planting of a spermatophore with (*right*) one planted.

deposit the sperm in the open air. Through this latter peculiarity we have the transition from external fertilization. It is true that the spermatophores are not always deposited on the ground. There are numerous instances in which they are transferred directly to the female body.

The structure of the spermatophore is exceedingly varied. In the simplest form it consists of tiny drops of semen enclosed in a delicate membrane and planted in the ground by means of a long stem (see Fig. 34). The spermatophore may on the other hand constitute a highly complicated apparatus. In the octopus (*Sepia*) it is explosive and at the decisive moment hurls forth the entire store of sperms.

The distribution of spermatophores in the animal kingdom is very

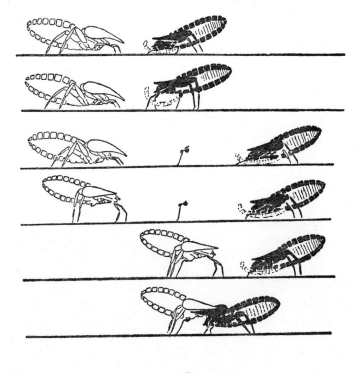

FIG. 35. Mating of the book scorpion, *Chelifer cancroides* (male black). The spermatophores and ramshorn-like organs of the male can be recognized in the picture.

remarkable, for they are limited to animals at the middle level of organization. They are not found in the lowest or in the highest animals. In the first named, it may well be that spermatophores constitute beyond doubt a complication, we might almost say a technical improvement, not to be expected in the lower animals. That they are not found in the highly developed animals follows from the fact that they almost never occur where true copulatory organs exist. As a rule they are found only where fertilization takes place without those.★

To explain a few cases in greater detail, we can best start with the primitive insects, of which the *Collembola* or springtails have solved the sexual question, without doubt in the happiest manner. At the onset of the mating season, the males deposit their spermatophores anywhere on the ground. These are, as we have already seen, tiny seminal drops enveloped in a delicate membrane and poised on a gossamer stem. We must now visualize that at suitable spots, at that time of year, many of these pretty structures will be found close together. The female later perambulates the pleasure garden in search of these remarkable fruits and receives the droplet in her sexual opening. That is all! We see, therefore, that the two partners in this curious business do not meet at all; the paternity in each case remains anonymous and the problem of choosing a mate is cunningly avoided. The naturalist must recognize also that there is in this case no question of a sexual selection. It is interesting that precisely the same behaviour holds good in a totally different group of animals, namely the mites, and especially in the moss mites (Oribatidæ). The actual position assumed by the animal in depositing the spermatophores is shown in Fig. 34. One male is able to deposit a fair number of such droplets. In one instance, thirty were counted in four days, all of which reached their goal. The females run over the spermatophores with the genital cleft open and tear off the heads, presumably with the three points of their ovipositors, the bare stalk remaining behind.

Matters are rather more complicated for the book scorpion, a pretty little spider that in temperate latitudes may be found most frequently in the dry leaves of a woodland but sometimes also in houses. Here the spermatophore is not deposited haphazardly, but only when a female ready for mating is present. The taking up of the spermatophore is guided by the male. The animals seize each other with their pincers and

★ Exceptions not further discussed here are found among insects.

an amusing tug-of-war ensues, until the male walking backward
succeeds in dragging the female over the spot where the spermatophore
lies. In contrast to the *Collembola* and Oribatids there is here, then, in
spite of the spermatophores having been placed on the ground, a
definite relation between two individuals, and a definite love play
leading to the consummation of the sexual act. Special sensory and
physiological equipments seem to ensure the success of the whole
process. During the love play the males extrude two singular long
funnels, the so-called ramshorns. We do not know their significance,
but must presume that some sort of scent exudes from them which
induces in the female a willingness to mate.

Tailed amphibians behave similarly in some respects. Since the newt
is referred to in another place we will here have a look at the spotted
salamander, in which mating takes place on land. The male pushes
himself under the female from behind so that she is upon his back, and
he holds her forelegs fast in his. In this situation the spermatophores
are deposited on the ground. As the male creeps sideways from under
the female, she settles with her cloacal cleft precisely where the
spermatophore has been set on the ground and there takes it up. The
Molge waltli behaves in precisely the same way. In the tailed
amphibians the spermatophore may in certain rare cases be transferred
direct from the male cloaca to the female, so that the external deposition
is dispensed with. This is so in *Euproctus asper*, in which the male clasps
the female for hours until in fact the transference has been effected.
The method by which squids transfer the semen in spermatophores
differs from anything else found in the animal kingdom. Here it takes
place by means of a specially developed arm called a hectocotylus. In
Loligo pealii, disporting themselves on the high seas, the male clasps the
female from beneath with his arms. Having got a firm hold he reaches
with the hectocotylus into the mouth of his own funnel and withdraws
the spermatophores from it. These have emerged simultaneously from
the sexual opening, and are lying in the so-called mantle cavity which
leads to the exterior by way of the funnel. The hectocotylus, now filled
with spermatophores, is inserted with the greatest speed into the female
mantle cavity and there the spermatophores are emptied. The whole
process is over in a few seconds.

Even more peculiar is the behaviour of the eight-armed cephalopods.
The typical position in mating, in which the animals are far apart from
each other, and in which only the outstretched hectocotylus reaches

into the female's mantle cavity, is shown in Fig. 36. The transference here of the spermatophores is brought about by an undulatory contractile movement of the hectocotylus. In this case the male is the only one to participate. In the remarkable *Argonauta*, on the other hand, the unprecedented happens, in that the very much metamorphosed hectocotylus is detached from the body of the male as soon as it is filled with spermatophores, and makes its own way independently. It is

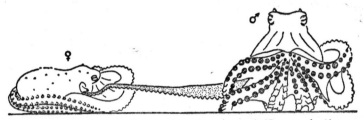

FIG. 36. Mating position of an eight-armed octopus, sepia (*Octopus vulgaris*).

deposited somewhere on the body of the female and eventually arrives in her mantle cavity by its own sinuous movements.

The mating position

The bodily union of the two partners forms the first climax of sexual life; the birth of the offspring forms the second. For the naturalist the first process, usually known as mating or copulation, is especially interesting for the reason that it reveals the most complicated instinctive actions of the whole animal realm.

This is not the place to go farther into the problem of instinct as such, but it should be emphasized that instinctive acts are those which are inherited, are in no case learnt and are peculiar to each species. Each individual of a given species carries out instinctive acts as laid down for that species; individual actions, such as those which in us are guided by reason, do not exist.

This applies in full measure to the assumption of the posture for mating. Its complicated nature is shown in that the male animal, who in his ordinary life disposes of only simple performances like running, swimming and feeding, now suddenly has the most precise knowledge of the anatomy of his female partner, and in that manifests astonishing skill. Let us examine this a little more in detail in the special case of the spiders. The sexual opening of the female spiders lies almost entirely under a cover, the so-called epigyne, hidden away far forward on the ventral side of the massive abdomen. The male spider knows quite accurately that he must deposit his store of semen with his feelers at this spot and nowhere else. For all other beasts the same may be said, and here we face a problem in animal behaviour which will be hard to solve.

In the following we will make only a short survey of the animal kingdom as a whole and extract a few of the most remarkable facts. The only instance in which the rule is broken, and in which no typical mating posture exists, is in rotifers, microscopic worm-like animals which can be usually found in large numbers and numerous species in our standing waters. The very small males attach themselves at some point firmly to the much larger female and pierce the wall of the female's body with their dagger-like penis. Thus the semen is not introduced into the sexual canals of the female as is customary almost everywhere else, but is simply injected into the spacious body cavity at random. From there the spermatozoa must find their own way to the eggs, a way which it is true is very short.

Among the worm-like animals we will examine further only the threadworms or roundworms, to which belong all sorts of human parasites like the nematodes and the trichinæ. In these animals there is a marked sexual dimorphism, which relates not only to the size of the body but also to the position of the internal organs. The sexual opening of the female worm lies somewhat in the foremost third of the body, whereas in the male it is found at the hind end of the body. The mating posture is thus mechanically determined.

An incredible variety of mating postures is found also in arthropods, with which we will deal a little more thoroughly. From the morphological point of view one can first of all divide these into two according to whether the mating is carried out with typical mating organs or with other instruments not belonging to the actual genital apparatus, and which are then called pseudo-mating organs or gonopods. Let us take these latter first.

Under this heading a few very peculiar things can be combined. In the common tick (*Ixodes ricinus*) the male proceeds as follows. He first pushes himself beneath the female and inserts his proboscis, which is his sole means of taking in nourishment, deep into the female genital opening for the purpose of enlarging it. When this is done, he creeps a bit farther forward and deposits a packet of semen, enclosed in an envelope, in the vicinity of the female opening. He now reverts to his original position and with all manner of contortions pushes the mass of sperm into her genital opening. A similar procedure is, in fact, found in other mites. For instance, in *Hæmogamasus hirsutus* the male grips the pear-shaped seminal capsule issuing from his genital opening with his cheliceræ and carries it to the female sexual opening, where he empties it.

Millipedes or diplopoda employ two pairs of modified running legs, this time true gonopods which lie on the seventh segment, for the insertion of the sperm. Their genital opening lies on the third segment. Before the mating the sperm must be transferred from the genital opening to the gonopods. This is done by a peculiar rolling up of the fore-part of the body. The position of the body during mating differs from species to species. In *Polydesmus* the animals are in contact along the whole length of the body, with the abdomens turned towards each other, and clasp each other mutually with their numerous running legs. Recent studies of the behaviour of *Blaniulus* show it to be quite different. Here the mating is preceded by a real flirtation, during which the animals with their long bodies entwined turn round in a tight circle on the spot. This may last half an hour. When the male has brought the semen on to his gonopods he entwines the fore-part of the female's body by forming a real knot, leaving the rear part of the body free to assume any desired position (see Plate XVI).

True gonopods also play an important part in the mating of the decapod crustacea, for example the river crayfish, crabs and so on.

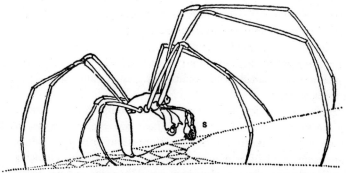

FIG. 37. Male spider, preparation for mating. He has spun a small web, deposited a small drop of semen upon it (*s*) and picks it up with one palp.

On the whole the process here is much simpler. The first abdominal legs of the male are transformed into a kind of tube. These are inserted into the female genital opening, the remaining legs being used for swimming. Since the male genital opening lies immediately at the base of these tubes, the transference of the semen proceeds in the easiest possible way (see Plate XIV). In spiders the males must carry out extensive preparations before they are ready for mating. Male spiders

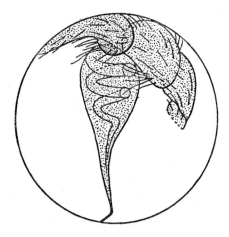

FIG. 38. Tip of the feeler (palp) of a male spider.

have no penis. On the contrary, the outer joint of the second feeler has been modified for the transference of the semen. Their often very complicated structure cannot, for reasons of space, be described in detail. In the simplest form the end joint is pear-shaped and contains a sort of capillary tube which serves to take up the drop of semen (see Fig. 38).

To fill the feeler the male spins a small horizontal web consisting generally of only a few strands, and presses his genital opening against it with strong up and down movements until a small drop of semen emerges and sticks to the web. As soon as this occurs the feelers, usually alternately, are dipped into the semen until they are full. Only when this has been done is the emotion of love awakened in the male and he thereupon resorts to his bride.

This account is merely an outline. In fact there is an incredible number of variations. Each species has its own peculiarities, with the description of which one could fill many pages.

We have now described two different ways of taking the semen into the feelers: one, the direct method in which the feeler is dipped straight into the drop, and the other indirect, to be observed in most running spiders, in which the collection of semen is effected through the meshes of a web. But there are many other variations. To complete the picture, in the following account we will only describe the peculiar conduct of the large tropical bird-eating spiders: they belong to the second group. In these, the male makes a fairly large flat web, bites a hole in it with his jaws and through this hole reaches the underside of the web. Hanging upside down he now presses his genital opening against the edge of the web for some half an hour or so. After that, movements cease and a large drop of semen appears on the underside of the web about a quarter of an inch from the edge. The male now crawls to the upper side and dips very rapidly, with his two feelers alternately, into the seminal drop. It is nevertheless two to three hours before the entire seminal mass has disappeared into the antennæ. Having finished the work the male destroys his web and is now prepared for mating.

In spiders, the process of mating is always the same, but the positions assumed for it are of every conceivable kind. When mating takes place on level ground it very often happens that the female stands erect and turns her abdominal side towards the male in such a way that he finds the epigyne easily. There are, however, quite different positions. In the crab spider it develops into a remarkable embrace in which both animals may be facing the same way, or else the male may stand transversely to the female. In web-spinning spiders the variations are very

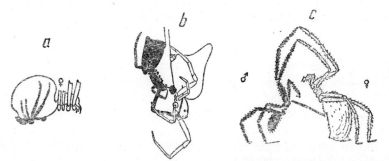

FIG. 39. Mating positions of various spiders: (a) *Misumena* (crab spiders); (b) *Sybota producta*; (c) *Filistata insidiatrix*. In all these diagrams the male is black.

great. Here also we find mainly attitudes in which the two sexes either face the same way or in opposite directions. All this, however, is only remarkable if it is clearly remembered that we are dealing with sequences of movement determined by heredity. One species does it one way, another does it another way. The male of a given species must fulfil the rites prescribed for his species in every detail. For us these matters are difficult to understand, because most spiders, at least the web-spinning spiders, have very poor eyesight and cannot therefore control their movements at all by sight. Although no experiments have been made on this it is abundantly clear that the entire mating could proceed in the dark as well as it does in the light. It must then be mainly by touch that the animals attain the correct relative positions.

Apart from the mating posture there are numerous other peculiarities. The mating may take place on the ground or on the courting thread or at the centre of the web. The male can, during this, insert one antenna or both together, both once only or there may be many insertions. When we further consider that in some species the pair hold each other fast with their jaws, in others the female is spun into a web and in yet others the male is devoured for breakfast in the end, then we see that the love life of spiders provides a quite considerable number of permutations. We will return later to some of these details.

Let us now turn our backs on the spiders and pass to the realm of the insects. Here also we may place at the beginning a group which in its mating employs atypical means. These are the dragon-flies, these kings of the air whose graceful flight over the water must have been seen by everyone with wonder. Amongst other things we may probably have seen two dragon-flies flying about together in a remarkably odd attitude. Whoever has seen this has been able to follow a small part at least of the love life of these beautiful creatures with his own eyes.

In dragon-flies the genital opening, as is universal in insects, is at the rear end of the abdomen. But for reasons which we nowadays still do not understand, the semen is not transferred directly from the male to the female genital opening but first of all to another part of the male body which lies in the second and third segments of the abdomen, that is to say, well forward. The structure of these parts is very complicated. The third segment supplies the so-called seminal bladder into which the semen is first pumped; the second segment carries a spermatophore into which the semen overflows, to go finally from there into the female vagina. Only when this is noted can one understand the very peculiar attitude which is assumed by the dragon-flies during mating. The males have, at their rear end, a pair of strong pincers. With these the lovelorn male seizes a passing female by the back of the neck, behind the head. The transfer of semen into the above-mentioned apparatus at the fore-end of the abdomen takes place in some dragon-flies before this act, in others not until after, which explains the remarkable attitude which we see during this phase. Only now does the female commence to take an active part. When the male, after transferring the semen forward, again extends the rear part of his body, she curls hers so far forward that her gential opening touches the region of the male's second and third abdominal segments. What happens there need not be followed in all its details. When the spermatophore situated on the second segment is filled it stretches away from the body and can now be inserted directly into the vagina (see Plate XVI).

In the remaining insects we are dealing, always, with a true coitus, in which actual mating organs belonging to the genital apparatus function. The structure of these organs is very complicated and cannot

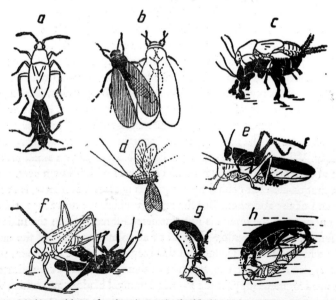

FIG. 40. Mating positions of various insects (males black): (a) bug (Aphanus); (b) whitefly Trialeurodes); (c) mole cricket (Gryllotalpa); (d) mayfly (Cloeon); (e) field grasshopper (Schistocera); (f) true grasshopper (Deciticus); (g) louse (Pediculus); (h) margined water-beetle (Dytiscus).

PLATE XV.

Fighting fish. "Dominant" attitude of the males.

Coitus position of dogfish.

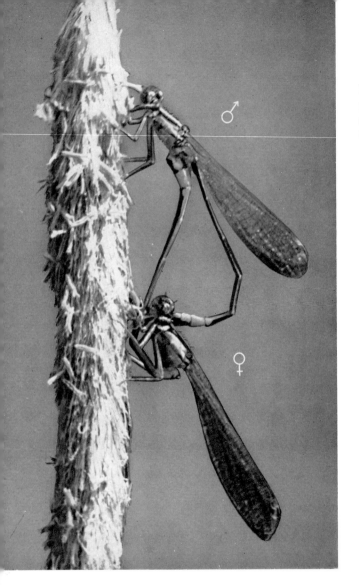

Plate XVI.

Mating position of dragon-flies, male above, female below.

♂

♀

Love embrace of two millipedes (*Blaniulus*).

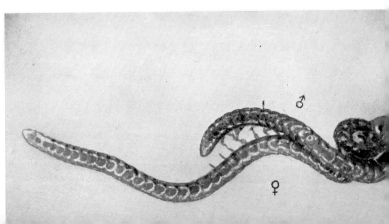

♂

♀

be discussed more closely here. The mating attitudes of insects are very varied. In butterflies, many bugs, caddis-flies and others the opposed position is typical. The creatures sit on the same leaf or on a tree trunk, but their heads are in opposite directions. In most beetles, orthoptera, flies and others, on the other hand, we find an attitude in which either the male sits on the female's back or vice versa.

In the mole cricket and other crickets, for instance, the female paradoxically sits on top, whilst in the grasshopper the male is on top. For the student of behaviour these are quite different things; from the morphological point of view, however, there is nothing in it. One has only to imagine the upper animal turned backward through 180 degrees and one gets a position that can frequently be observed in cockchafers: both creatures are opposed to each other but their position is "inverted", in that the back of one is upward—that of the other is directed downward.

Mating is not always without danger. It is reported of an ancient Neapolitan queen that although she was very liberal indeed with her charms each one who gained her favours was sewn into a sack in the morning and cast into the sea. Amongst animals many bridegrooms fare no better. Many a one having enjoyed life must suffer the bitter end of being devoured. The most notorious husband-murderesses are found amongst the spiders. Nevertheless, this assertion must not be applied too generally. In the majority of cases the affair passes off peacefully and the two partners separate with the utmost goodwill. But in some species, particularly where the female is very much larger (*Argiope bruennichi*, *Cyrtophora citricola*), it is simply part of the pre-ordained ceremony of mating that the male, after having emptied the second feeler, is devoured. The males have developed certain protective instincts against this unamiable conclusion to the mating; the male encloses the female completely in a web before the mating to impede her movements somewhat, but it seems that this precautionary measure does not always succeed. Of our native spiders the garden spider occasionally, though not always, pursues a policy of mate-murder, and it is very amusing to observe with what caution the male approaches the very much bigger female. The language of spiders belongs to the sphere of the sense of touch. A delicate tug at the threads of the web tells whether the Mighty One is ready for mating or not. At the slightest sign that the answer is in the negative the unbidden bridegroom hastily descends by a thread, to renew his efforts after a time. In the spider *Argiope lobata*, the male escapes the fate of being eaten alive in a very remarkable manner. He dies of exhaustion with unfailing punctuality at the conclusion of mating.

In insects also there are various husband-murderesses. The best known are the species of mantis, which in view of this conduct do not unconditionally deserve the name of "praying" mantis. In these beasts of prey the female is about double the size of the male. Here again the males have developed instincts to escape the murderous grip of the predatory legs of their opposite sex. Before the mating the male lurks in the immediate vicinity of the female for a long time and at a favourable opportunity quickly jumps on her back. In spite of this precaution it very often happens that he is devoured after a mating or even during it.

Some ant-lions behave equally malignantly towards their males. The name is somewhat misleading and refers only to the larval life, for the adult insects resemble dragon-flies in many respects. In some species husband-murder seems to occur with regularity. The difference in temperament between the sexes is also shown in the following experiment. If two males are imprisoned together, nothing in particular happens; the creatures live peacefully with one another. But two females in the same situation immediately take up an aggressive attitude and only quieten down gradually. Should one place a fecund female and a male together, however, then the male is instantly devoured.

It is pertinent to philosophize a little on this singular custom of husband-murder. The blood-lust of the female is connected with her strong need for albumen in consequence of her rapid egg production. For the same reason female gnats are compelled to suck blood, for without this blood transfusion they cannot lay eggs. That is how the problem appears from the female's point of view. As regards the males, we find the old law confirmed that Nature does not concern herself with the individual but only with the species. When the male has unloaded his store of semen at the correct spot he has discharged his duty to his kind.

This philosophy of Nature, that the females are more important than the males, is everywhere confirmed. The amorous death of the drone belongs to it. Certainly he is not eaten, but when the animals separate after mating a portion of his inner organs is torn out and he dies.

For the rest, we will take but a brief look at the vertebrates. Sharks behave very peculiarly. In contrast to bony fish, they are fertilized internally and in many cases are viviparous. As shown in the lower photograph in Plate XV of a dogfish, the male of this species encircles the female transversely. During this highly remarkable, attractive and graceful movement the cloacæ are pressed together so that the transfer of semen into the female cloaca is easily accomplished. The fact that in male sharks a part of each pelvic fin has been transformed into genital organs has often led to a misinterpretation, since according to our definition they should be looked upon as gonopods, that is, as pseudo-genital organs. Actually they are only auxiliary organs. One of the two may be inserted in the female cloaca and serves to enlarge it. The end parts, strengthend by various skeletal portions, can be spread out by a strong extensor muscle. Only when this has been done does the male thrust the genital papilla, into which the outlets of the seminal ducts open, out of his own cloaca into the now extended cloaca of the female.

The mating posture of frogs and toads must be familiar to everyone. The male, usually the smaller, jumps upon the female's back and embraces her with his forelegs (see Plate XIV). The basis of the instinctive act is a simple reflex, the so-called clasping reflex, which is released from the spinal cord. In toads the males are carried about in this fashion for many hours until the female prepares to visit a suitable piece of water to spawn. Conditions in the African clawed toad are particularly remarkable. The female is several times the larger, and although it is true the male need not fear to be eaten, nevertheless certain precautions seem to be necessary in view of the disparity in size. In any case the male knows how to wrap the colossal female round himself so that an akinesis, a complete immobility ensues, which facilitates the further proceedings.

So far as reptiles are concerned only lizards and snakes have been examined up to now in any detail. With them it is characteristic that the males have two genital organs, a right and a left, of which, however, only one is used at a time. This is probably related to the peculiar mating position, which is as a rule as shown in the illustration of a viviparous lizard (*Lacerta vivipara*). The male stands more or less square to the female, as we have seen in sharks, which also possess two lateral genital organs.

A remarkable phenomenon accompanying the mating of reptiles is that the male in many species bites the female during the act, and, indeed, quite severely, for the wounds can be recognized easily for a long time after. This, to us, somewhat sadistic method of carrying on is peculiar to the species and hereditarily fixed. The wall lizard bites the flank of the female and the remainder of our native lizards behave in precisely the same way. The blindworm seizes the female with his teeth, either by the head or neck. In snakes this somewhat painful ceremony is also found, although not in venomous snakes. The latter is biologically intelligible since otherwise they would soon have been self-exterminated. Amongst our snakes it is reported of the false coral snake that the male seizes the female's neck firmly with his teeth. The viper, like the ringed snake, the adder or the tessellated snake, does not.

The actual act of mating also varies somewhat from one species to another. The male wall lizard bites the female in the flank in the manner described, then pushes his body underneath that of the female so that his cloacal cleft comes to lie in opposition to that of the female and insertion of one penis is readily accomplished. In those snakes in which the tail is quite short, and the cloaca as a consequence lies well back along the body, the process is rather different.

In the ringed snakes, which before mating indulge in odd jerking movements, the two first lie alongside each other. Then the male pushes the root of his tail below that of the female, so that there again the cloacæ lie in opposition to each other.

In birds the mating act is one of the greatest simplicity. In general it proceeds so that the male climbs upon the female's back, hence the expression to "tread", and, in this position, frequently accompanied by beating his wings, carries out the transfer of semen. Since most birds have no penis other arrangements are needed. Both animals protrude the outermost part of the cloaca, the so-called proctodæum, in the shape of a tube. These tubes are pressed closely together, so that the semen can be squirted directly from the male's cloaca into that of the female. The whole process lasts only a few seconds. The attitude of the female varies during this. Most females lie flat on the ground, but in some large birds such as the stork or the condor they remain standing.

A very peculiar mating posture is shown by the great crested grebe. The female lies flat on the nest, the male standing stiffly erect and beating his wings forward, no doubt to preserve his balance.

Mating takes place either on land or in the water, according to the habits of the respective species. In some birds it may take place even in the air. This last seems only to have been determined with certainty for the swift (*Apus apus*). The prelude to mating here is when the female in flight and ahead slows down and starts to glide, whereupon the male lowers himself upon her back and concludes the transfer of semen.

An exception to the usual practice is shown by those birds which possess an actual penis. These are the ostriches, the duck family and a few smaller groups only. In contrast to the lizards and snakes, the bird's penis is a single structure. The mating act is exactly as usual.

The mating posture of mammals is in general very similar. The male rides up from behind and clasps the female's body with his fore-legs. The attitude of the female also varies here; she either lies or stands up. A different attitude is that of the beaver, where the beasts mate belly to belly in an erect position.

The duration of mating varies enormously. In the ruminants the whole thing lasts but a moment, as it does in the feline beasts of prey. The longest time is stated to be in kangaroos and bears, which remain in the mating position for three-quarters of an hour, and in ferrets where it averages two hours. It is not known to what these variations in time may be ascribed, but it may reasonably be assumed that several seminal emissions follow each other.

A peculiarity apparently confined to the big cats, and not found in the domestic cat, is that during coitus the male grips the female's scruff with gaping jaws. After numerous personal observations at the Berlin Zoo I have always regarded this as a precautionary measure to prevent her snapping at the decisive moment. On the other hand, leading experts assert that at the moment of ejection a bite at the neck really occurs which leaves scars for many a day. For this somewhat dubious caress his better half revenges herself after completion of the process with powerful blows. This can be especially easily observed in tigers. The male seems to know what to expect, for usually he withdraws from his righteous punishment with a mighty leap.

FIG. 41. Mating position, puma; (*right*) neckbite.

10

MARITAL COHABITATION

WE find in the animal world, irrespective of the systematic position, transitions from a completely solitary life in which the sexes meet only for a brief period for the purpose of mating, to the lasting association which is terminated only by death. The most intimate permanent association, moreover, is not found among the highest forms of life but in some very lowly forms among the worms. Naturally we cannot apply any psychological standard to these, and it would be absurd to speak of a marriage, but inseparable cohabitation is found here in its purest form. In a trematode worm (*Schistosomum hæmatobium*) parasitic in the blood-vessels of man we find males and females always in the closest embrace. The male in cross section is not round but is deeply hollowed out on his lower surface, and in this hollow (*canalis gynæcophorus*), which stretches from head to tail, the much more slender female rests (Fig. 42). The sexes of the trematode *Balfouria monogama* live equally closely joined, and complete their existence together in a narrow cyst inside their host. Another group of animals in which one finds such "inseparables" are the decapod crustacea. Of these there are some kinds (*Conchodytes, Pontonia*) where the two sexes wander into a sponge or a coral in couples while still very young. They then enter a prison from which they cannot escape once they have grown larger. Their conjugal fidelity is therefore not wholly voluntary.

(*a*) MARITAL LIFE OF INSECTS

Turning to the higher animals we may first remark that it is only among two groups, insects and vertebrates, that such a companionship is found; it is generally absent in spiders and completely absent in mollusca, though there are some exceptions.

Even in insects cohabitation is a great rarity. The most outstanding examples are provided, oddly enough, by dung beetles, which are regarded by the layman with particular disgust. In several species of *Geotrupes, Copris, Sisyphus*, the two sexes do not separate after mating, as is almost always the case in insects. The instinct to provide the offspring with food is enough to keep them together over the whole incubation period. In the chapter on the care of the young we will discuss these interesting matters more in detail.

In the very much more lowly termites we may also speak of a marital cohabitation. It seems fitting to describe the whole course of their sexual life at the same time. As is known, termites usually live in vast hordes, communally in one nest. It must also be mentioned that they are divided into various castes: breeders, workers, soldiers. At the beginning of the mating season, then, the winged breeders—the others

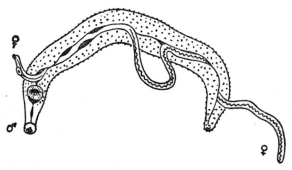

FIG. 42. Trematode worm, *Schistosomum hæmatobium*, male and female in normal juxtaposition.

are wingless—make an excursion from the nest, often in large swarms. They may travel various distances, in some species only a few yards, in the large powerful flyers to as much as several miles. This flight is no marriage flight as in bees or ants; no mating takes place during it. With a few exceptions males and females do not meet yet. The flight in general serves only to spread the species widely. When the flight is over and the creatures have alighted, they first do something extremely remarkable, one may say unprecedented: they shed their wings, a preparation for their approaching subterranean existence. For the rest, the various species behave very differently, and we will pick out some examples of particularly characteristic behaviour. In *Calotermes* matters develop very quickly. Should two insects of different sexes meet during the active creeping about which always follows the landing, they will place themselves head to head, feel each other with palps and feelers, and having come to an agreement the female will turn about and begin an activity which is the most characteristic of the whole sexual life of the termite, that is the "wedding promenade". The female leads in this, and the male follows so closely as to touch the rear tip of her body with his head. This march, which occurs in all termites, may last several hours and it ends when the female has found a suitable spot for the founding of the nest. In *Reticulitermes lucifugus* the opening ceremonies are somewhat different. Here the female, as soon as she has shed her wings, assumes a peculiar alluring posture in which she raises her abdomen vertically. Probably the males are thereby attracted by some scent or other; in any case, the wedding promenade commences as soon as a male approaches her.

In some other species, for instance in *Pseudacanthotermes*, it does in fact come to a wedding flight which may be compared with that of a bee. The breeders of this species take off from the nest in masses and fly all together straight up for thirty to forty-five feet. The male now grabs a female in flight, clings tightly to her and sheds his wings actually during the flight. Although burdened with the weight of the male the female continues her flight and sheds her wings on alighting.

Having chosen the position of the nest the common task of all the termites begins forthwith. Now is the time to dig the nuptial chamber, a heavy job which takes one to two days. Only when the entire work has been completed does the mating take place, in some species during the first few days, in others only after ten to fifteen days.

(b) MARITAL LIFE OF VERTEBRATES

Surprisingly there is no marital life at all in two large sections of the vertebrates, the amphibians and the reptiles. It is not possible to provide an explanation for this; we can but accept the fact. On the other hand, a marital coexistence is widespread among birds and mammals.

Mating in fishes

Actually, wedded life is not on a much higher plane in fishes than in insects. Nor is it much more frequent. In most species the two animals separate immediately after spawning. In fishes also there is no question of a personal bond between two individuals, but solely of a common task in the care of the brood. According to which sex takes care of the brood we speak of father-, mother- or parent-families. We may select *Hemichromis bimaculatus* as an example. The first step to the forming of couples consists here again in the male finding a fixed base and thereafter regarding it as his private domain from which he chases all others away. Even the gravid females fare no better; they also are driven from his territory. But in contrast to the males, one particular gravid female determined to mate with this particular male will return again and again in spite of repeated rebuffs. At last after many visits the male's opposition abates; he tolerates her in his domain for longer periods until finally he allows her to remain permanently. As soon as this happens she takes part in the defence of the territory, and they have now become mates. The spawning, which will not be discussed further here, takes place during the ensuing days and then the care of the brood begins. That we are justified in speaking here of a marital life is shown by the parents thereafter remaining together and, usually alternately, renewing the supply of clean water for the eggs by gently fanning with their pectoral fins, cleansing the eggs of débris and guarding the territory. Generally a certain division of labour occurs, at all events after a short period, the female remaining more in the vicinity of the eggs whilst the male tends to range the periphery of his kingdom driving off other fish.

These fishes relieve each other quite punctually at the egg-watching, so that it only rarely happens that the spawning-ground remains unguarded for a short time. When the young are hatched a new phase of life commences also for the parents, insofar that now the whole family go on excursions together. The youngsters then conduct themselves comparatively independently by forming themselves into a loose swarm, frequently preceding the parents. But at each hint of danger they rapidly return to the vicinity and safety of their parents. The parents, however, do something else besides. In particular the father, who perpetually swims round the periphery of the shoal, shows an instinct to snap up with his mouth youngsters who have strayed and return them to the swarm.

The termination of this harmonious family life takes place automatically when the young have grown and become more independent. Doubtless the protective instincts of the parents gradually get duller, and it may even happen that now and then they devour one of their own offspring. It is of interest, and has often been observed, that the parent fish having once concluded such a seasonal marriage very soon again proceed to propagation. It may happen that the pairing may persist over several seasons, but in fishes a truly permanent matrimony probably never occurs.

Mating in birds

In this group of animals every form and permutation of the matrimonial state may be found. Complete solitude occurs in some kinds of fowls, for example in grouse. When the courtship is over and the cock has done his duty, he proceeds on his way and does not bother in the least about what becomes of the young or even about nest-building. Other examples of the solitary state are provided by some snipe, probably also birds of paradise and cuckoos. In the latter this is obviously connected with the fact that they are relieved from any sort of duty towards their progeny, for there is neither nest-building nor parental care among these brood parasites whose eggs are laid in other birds' nests. All the same, solitude is in general the exception among birds. In most birds one finds true matrimony and, indeed, always monogamy. Polygamy, which is found so often in mammals, such that one male holds sway over many females, is nowhere found in birds. In a very few cases there is polyandry.

Monogamous matrimony may be divided into the seasonal and perpetual. Both are, however, connected by fluid transitions. The seasonal marriage comes to an end at latest when the business of rearing the brood is finished. Sometimes, however, it ends considerably earlier. In this category the ducks are easily foremost, in some species the drake loosing his ties as early as when the first egg has been laid, in others when the brood is hatched. In most nidicolous birds, including most of our songsters, which are helpless when hatched and for some time after and thus have to remain in the nest, the bond persists until the young have outgrown their parents' care.

Permanent matrimony is reported of many large birds, such as storks, birds of prey, parrots, swans, geese, etc. For many reasons this view must, however, be taken with a grain of salt. Most of the earlier field observations can hardly be regarded as reliable, since they were made without the aid of ringing, that is to say without any real identification of individuals. We may distinguish between two forms of permanent bond, that which is dissolved after the brooding, in which nevertheless the same pair come together again at the next mating time, and that in which the couple continue to cohabit throughout the year. In the past the duration of matrimony was evidently assessed on the fact that the birds returning northward from their winter quarters always return to their previous nesting site. The rule therefore would be that the pairs will again meet, and if this were observed for a number of years we would arrive at a fictitious permanent marriage. It may, however, take another course. The stork has been pretty closely watched, and of him it has recently been said that he works on the basis of "First come, first served". The male stork is wont to arrive first at the nest in the spring, and usually the old hen will follow fairly soon afterwards. If, however, she is delayed, then he will take into his nest the first suitable hen which appears before him. Marital fidelity would then, it seems, have to be discounted. Very likely more detailed observation of some other large birds will produce similar disappointments. True permanent lifelong wedlock is reported of parrots, eagles, ravens, some owls, swans and grey lag-geese. In the last named, marital fidelity is obviously connected with the circumstance that care of the brood lasts an extremely long time; it goes on for a whole year, so that the pair will still be together when the next mating season comes round. Regarding parrots it should be emphasized that these birds are typically not migratory, but always remain together. Thus circumstances facilitate the contraction of a permanent bond. For the rest it may well be doubted whether the necessary field observations exist to prove a true permanent bond. In pigeons also the birds remain together after the breeding period.

A rare fact sometimes observable in birds is a mating between two representatives of different species. In the Schönbrunn Zoological Gardens a faithful union persisted between a white and a black stork, although numerous individuals of both species were present in the large aviary. Every spring these birds built their nest and attempted to rear a family, in which, however, they never succeeded. Among geese similar observations have been made.

These matters are of special interest, for they prove that in the mating of birds a union of two beings is actually involved. This is important, because it is sometimes asserted that it is only their common efforts at nest-building and in the rearing of their young which maintain the bond between birds. Heinroth writes of the great spotted woodpecker: "Man and wife seem to be continually in a state of mutual hostility. One has the feeling that to each of the two birds it is shocking that in the entire business of breeding and feeding of the young another bird should interfere. It is similar in many insectivorous birds." Against this explanation and in favour of a real affection between the two is the abundant evidence of tenderness which may be seen between many paired birds.

Preening each other's plumage is the best-known expression of these marital feelings. This has been seen not only among ravens but also in many parrots, in wood ducks and in other birds.

This side of family life seems to be developed particularly strongly in parrots, which it is generally agreed, live in a strict monogamy. At the time of the mating season these feelings become stronger. The two birds then never leave each other for a moment and usually sit quietly

FIG. 43. Raven, endearments (preening after pairing).

cuddled together. Of the cockatoos it is said that they mutually embrace, actually throwing their wings about each other, and kiss each other like two lovers. The latter must not be taken too literally with these hard-beaked birds.

Yet there is also among the birds a less pretty side to the marital cohabitation. Not even in animals is fidelity always sublime beyond any doubt. It is reported of the drake that long after the mating he takes the greatest delight in pursuing strange ducks and if possible doing them violence. If a pair of ducks have alighted upon some small bay in a larger sheet of water, one usually sees her busily dipping for food whilst he eagerly glances round. If at a distance of some hundred yards, perhaps, a second pair descends, then it is not long before the first male swims suddenly and as swiftly as he can towards the strange duck, who oddly enough is not protected by her mate. When she sees the danger she suddenly takes wing and a frantic chase ensues in which the pursued spirals to ever greater heights. Her mate, who at first watches this drama idly, finally follows her and so one sees two drakes after one duck. This has been frequently explained by supposing the poor creature to be pestered by two suitors. Actually, however, only one is in action. After a time, when things have come to this pass, the first drake usually abandons the chase and alights again in the vicinity of his own mate, who fortunately seems to take no notice of all these goings on.

Cases of jealousy have also, however, been observed in birds. If one keeps two hen parrots together in a cage they can quite easily become accustomed to one another and live happily together. If now a male is introduced, a mating is soon being arranged with one of the birds, with the result that the other hen is filled with a seething jealousy. Cruel bites may then be inflicted and usually the wedded bird loses some feathers.

In some birds an interval occurs before the actual mating which we can only describe as a period of betrothal. The birds have indeed paired off, but the business of reproduction has its beginning considerably later. The best-known cases are amongst wild geese, ducks and daws. The daws become betrothed in the spring following their birth and betrothal lasts just a year. Ducks become engaged in the autumn, remain together during the winter and celebrate their marriage in the spring. The wild geese behave similarly. It is very remarkable that we know of nothing like it in any other group of animals.

Besides the betrothal, described in the above cases as customary, there are other forms of approach between the sexes. In the yellow bunting one may perhaps put it that the two flirt for some time. A male flirts with several females and the same female may be found in the territory first of this male, then of another. They thus get to know each other gradually, and from this there develops in time a preference for one particular member of the opposite sex, which eventually leads to pairing and mating.

Mating in mammals

The mating of mammals is distinguished from that of birds in an extraordinary number of ways. Most authorities assume that strictly monogamous mating does not occur in mammals at all, or at most for a short time only. The male mammal tends to be polygamous, and the solitary habit is widespread. These things are related, almost certainly, to the fact that the care of the young can only begin when the young are born, which is often after a lapse of many months. A common duty binding the partners together immediately after mating, as in the nest-building and incubation of birds, is therefore absent. The male has nothing to do and so he goes his way.

Examples of complete solitude are seen in the hamster, the mole and the hare, and, farther afield, in the tiger. It is always the animals which outside the rutting season are typically solitary that behave thus.

On the other hand, many mammals are communal animals which prefer to go about together in herds. The composition of such herds is, however, extraordinarily varied and is by no means always connected with the sexual life. The desire for company often brings animals of like sex together. A typical example of this is the wild pig. Some of their herds consist of adult females and older youngsters only, and there are also herds in which a number of boars have banded together. A similar social order is found also in the fallow deer. In them, the younger males, which have not yet grown their palmate antlers, remain, outside the rutting season, with the females and the fawns, other herds consist only of antlered bucks. Nevertheless this formation into companies can also be connected with a different ecological behaviour. In the large wild sheep of Central Asia, whose chief enemy is the wolf, the females and their young stay on precipitously steep slopes, where wolves are unable to reach them; the strong rams, however, who do not need to fear wolves, collect in herds in the deeper and flatter valley bottoms where they find richer grazing. In the bison the older beasts remain alone, outside the rutting season, the younger bulls forming a separate herd with the cows and calves.

The reverse of the herds, which have nothing to do with sexual cohabitation, are those in which mature animals of both sexes remain together throughout the year. In these there is generally one male king beast who takes charge and who has several females with him. Polygamy is thus very clearly indicated here. Delmont, who spent twenty years hunting big game in Africa and Asia, writes: "I had many opportunities of observing that to one lion there were several lionesses and their cubs. The cubs were not of the same age. I saw quite small babies a few weeks old and youths and maidens that had already passed their sixth month or even one year of age." Here, then, one can speak of a real family; it is not monogamous, however, but polygamous. That the lion makes a good head of a family can be convincingly proved in any zoo. The youngsters can play round about him quite safely when he is having his siesta, even climbing over him and tugging at his mane. He may growl peevishly now and then and may also push them off, if it becomes too much of a good thing, but that is all. A tiger would instantly make a meal of them.

Herds of similar composition are formed among many ungulates, for instance in deer or cattle. A normal herd of red deer consists of a king beast, several weaker stags, a larger number of female animals and their young (see Plate XIX). In the Cape buffalo it is the same, and wild horses can well be placed in this category.

The leadership varies in these herds. Among the antelopes it is in general an experienced old animal that leads. Among buffalo, horses and deer it is usually the strongest male. Their behaviour is, however, very varied.

It is interesting to consider what duties the males in such a herd carry out. The duties of the females are clearly prescribed by the care and rearing of their young. It behoves the males, one would assume, to protect the herd against enemies. This in fact is so in buffalo and wild horses. Anyone who has wandered near a herd of grazing cattle will certainly have been impressed by the behaviour of the bull, who either advances upon the intruder with low bellows, or stands still, his head always turned towards the stranger following him with his eyes as far as possible. Major Wissmann, the old German pioneer, has given a lively account of the Cape buffalo's defence of his herd against a lion. When danger threatens and has been recognized in time the herd forms a close circle, horns directed outward, with the calves inside the ring. Only the leader remains outside the circle and advances on the foe with lowered head. One can see by the waving of the grass how the great cat takes flight from the powerful horns and gradually departs from the neighbourhood of the herd. We also know how the stallion stoutly defends the herd from wolves and other enemies. The stag, again, behaves quite differently, although he also possesses the necessary weapons. When the herd is about to leave the cover of a wood at dusk to find pasture in an open glade one sees an old beast emerge cautiously to ensure safety. Should the air be untainted then the rest follow step by step, and only after all of them are already standing in the open space does the antlered stag appear.

This procedure is an unusual experience in the animal world. It is easily possible that it has been developed in the course of centuries during which not the wolf or the bear but man has become the greatest danger to the red deer. The unremitting pursuit of antlered male deer may be the cause of the defence measures we have described.

For the rest the tyranny of the male leader is already felt in these mixed herds, and eventually leads in some cases to a true harem economy.

Let us consider the wild horses first.

Since the original wild horse is as good as extinct, as those which remain live in inaccessible places in Central Asia, we are restricted to observations made occasionally in special circumstances (such as the Duke of Croy's preserve in Westphalia, Ascania nova, etc.). The herds of horses running wild in the Bahamas do not seem to have been studied as yet.

It is remarkable that the original urges from a past of several millennia instantly re-emerge when horses, as happens in large preserves, revert in some measure to natural conditions. As already mentioned, the strongest stallion assumes the leadership. In him a series of different urges may be distinguished. The first very outstanding one, which seems to be more or less lacking in the other single-toed ungulates, is that of driving his mares together. The animal shows himself at his most handsome when at a fast trot he hurries towards the dispersed mares, circles them and greets them with whinneys.

Antonius (1937), to whom we are indebted for an excellent account of the behaviour of horses, mentions the magnificent verses of Homer in the sixth canto of the *Iliad*, thus:

> "As, when a stallion in his stable nourished with barley, from his crib boldly tears his halter and with stamping course hurries to the field, there to the laving of the lovely stream
>
> "Daring power, head carried high and about his shoulders flies the mane, but proud in the nobility of youth his limbs do bear him easily to the well-known meadow of the mares."

This splendid picture, which has been so often penetratingly depicted by artists, gives way to a somewhat less beautiful one when it occurs to the stallion to adjust differences of opinion, be it to chase a rival away or to bring a recalcitrant mare to reason. In these threatening attitudes, which are neither beautiful nor heroic, the stallion lowers his head at the full stretch of his neck to the ground, lays his ears back in the well-known manner of all animals with a mind to bite, and then attacks his foe with short galloping leaps. The lowering of the head to the ground

PLATE XVII.

Spiders' cocoon with hatched-
out young spiders.

Mating of the poplar moth,
Smerinthus populi. Female
above, male below.

PLATE XVIII.

Hippopotami enjoying a midday siesta. In zoos, animals are often forced into a permanent marriage which when running wild would usually only be a seasonal union. But even in this there are peaceful moments.

PLATE XIX. Herd of deer during the rutting season.

PLATE XX.

Female wolf spider, *Tarantula inquilina*, with young on her back.

Male sea-horse with full brood-pouch.

Male midwife toad with packet of eggs.

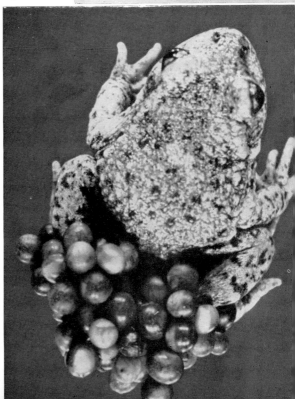

shows us clearly that this instinctive attitude was originally adapted to the driving off of enemies, amongst which the wolf in the wilderness most certainly occupied chief place. The lowering of the head can thus be satisfactorily explained as an attempt to protect the most sensitive part, the throat. The stallion assumes the same threatening attitude with a slanting, upward-cocked eye, which gives him a malicious appearance, when he drives his mares together. He does not by any means always stop at these threats and often the poor mares have to suffer painful correction. Heck (1937) gives such an excellent account of this that it is better to repeat it word for word:

"All naturally wild stallions which I have tended were in the habit of driving the herd of mares together. Some mares did not readily obey if, until then, they had not known herd life or the rule of a stallion. The stallion, however, very quickly convinced them that they must obey him; this was accomplished by lightning bites. Primitive stallions mostly bite the comb of the mane or more rarely the legs. Wounding of the body by bites is rare, but does occur. After the bite or even whilst chasing the mare he will turn like lightning and give the obstinate creature a kick with his hind legs."

Mares also defend themselves by lashing out. Experienced stallions, however, have a sound technique of suddenly jumping so close to the mare's body that she is no longer able to kick. If mares have been brought up in fear of a stallion then his look and expression suffice to bring them to obedience. Should a stallion become seriously angry with a mare or his herd of females, then his gestures become more pronounced. He drops his head so low that his lower lip nearly touches the ground. Then when he circles the herd of mares with outstretched neck and squints so furiously from down there at his ladies every mare knows that she must withdraw into the herd without delay.

Asses comport themselves quite differently to horses. They also have been little observed in the wild state. The main difficulty here again is that most species of wild asses have been almost exterminated. The only one of the earlier naturalists who was in a position to make adequate observations on them was Menges (1887), who was able to study Danakil and Somali asses in the wild. According to his excellent observations these African wild asses live in smallish troops led by an old mare. He-asses in these are most probably young animals. The mature males live separately from the females for the greater part of the year in smaller troops and only seek them during the rut. This explains why a donkey, unlike the horse stallion, has no urge at all to keep the herd together. He has only the instinct to perform the act of covering.

Deer seem generally to behave more courteously. Out of the rutting season the leading stag not only tolerates the lesser stags, as we have mentioned, but also leaves the herd for days on end, though he is always recognized when he returns. In the rutting season, of course, this behaviour changes, since the chief stag then sets about making himself paramount. The younger stags, which perhaps also would like an amorous adventure, are mercilessly hunted away, so that only females and youngsters remain in the herd.

In conclusion we will now look at a true harem economy which is found chiefly in the baboons and among some seals. The human harem, known to us through tales from the Orient, and the harem of the animal kingdom have one thing in common, namely the complete deprivation of rights for the women. The difference from the herd may well be that here is a case of real family grouping, except that usually a whole series of such families, each consisting of an old pasha, his horde of wives and their children, unites into a larger combination. In sacred baboons, where the males are double the size of the females and possess a fearsome dentition, one can see this communal life very well when they are in a zoological garden. One can be easily convinced that the old pasha exercises a real reign of terror. No other individual dares to accept food from visitors to the zoo if he is near. Everyone's eyes are on him to see whether he is approaching or what he is doing. He rules his troop by glances, grimaces and gestures. In the wild, in which these animals have on the whole not been sufficiently observed yet, the unfortunate females no doubt are somewhat better off because the space is greater and they are not continually under the control of their lord.

A specially regulated cohabitation is found in one of the larger animal classes and consists of thousands of individuals; these are the seals, particularly the fur seals (*Arctocephalus ursinus*). One cannot call such an aggregation either a herd or a pack; it is almost a nation. Here we have one advantage since every year we can observe afresh how the social order of the entire group is formed. On the approach of spring, the bulls appear first on their islands, some four weeks before the cows. They are tremendous fellows, exceeding by many times the size and weight of the females. Each one takes over a certain strip of territory which he thereafter rules and defends against all rivals.

There are no extraneous foes on these islands. The younger males which are not the equals of the adults must content themselves with a separate strip of ground. Neither can they later intrude on the preserves of the older animals, if they value their lives. On the other hand, they may by an unwritten law reach the sea by certain paths to enable them to feed on fishes. The old bulls do not eat at all during the period of propagation.

Some four weeks after the bulls the females appear in large hordes. The males swim to meet them, seize one or the other of them with their teeth and drag them ashore. It should not be assumed, however, that this is the sole method by which a harem is formed. It is more probable that many females themselves make a choice by seeking out the most splendid or handsome proprietor of a harem. The females cast a pup very soon after their arrival, but are then immediately covered anew. During the following period a very intimate family life develops, in which the father, it is true, plays a very passive part. He probably only takes care that none of his wives goes a-missing; he does not worry at all about the fate of his children.

As mentioned previously, many authors deny the existence of monogamy among mammals, but there seems to be no complete certainty on this point. There are observations which point to many animals, especially beasts of prey, being truly monogamous. We know something of this in the Canadian wolf. He seeks a mate in his third year, the parents and young often remaining together for two to three years. Meanwhile the family grows, and finally consists of five to eight adults and of the young of the last litter. Outwardly such a family naturally resembles one of the herds previously described. In reality, however, it has nothing in common with them. Occasionally, it is true, several such families may unite in a pack, but this occurs only for one particular hunting adventure, after which the families go their ways. The male wolf is said to care for the female in an exemplary manner whilst she is suckling her young.

Very little precise information is yet available about the matrimonial affairs of the large anthropoid apes. It is certainly possible that the chimpanzee is fundamentally polygamous. One usually meets bands with a leading male and three or four females. On the other hand gorillas may well be monogamous. The few observers who have had the good fortune to see this rare beast in freedom describe a very restricted family life: father, mother and one or two children. The mother looks after the children and gathers fruit from the trees. The father defends the family if danger threatens. Every night the gorilla family builds itself a nest in a tree, which, apart from its dimensions, resembles a stork's nest. The male, on the contrary, sleeps at the foot of the tree to protect his family from their main foe, the leopard. Whether this account, which is derived from one source only, is quite correct must await confirmation.

The gorilla, especially in the hill forests of Eastern Africa, is sometimes hunted by making a terrific noise in front of his previously discovered habitation. The courageous male sallies forth to drive away the disturbers of the peace and can then be easily killed.

II

BREEDING IN HERMAPHRODITES

IN a large number of animals the organs of both sexes are combined in one individual. Such animals are at once male and female, or, as we say, hermaphrodites. The question now arises as to how in such animals sexual life goes on. First of all, as we can imagine, most of what we have seen in animals with separate sexes no longer holds good. The hermaphrodite has after all everything within itself; it could fertilize its own eggs with its own spermatozoa. Were this really the way things go, the following would cease in sexual life: the seeking of mates, the inducement of readiness for mating, the complicated act of mating and so on. In reality things are quite different, and Nature has everywhere gone to the greatest trouble to prevent self-fertilization. Why this is so we humans have understood only after some very bitter experiences which we inflicted on ourselves by inbreeding. Marriages between relatives often give rise to misshapen or mentally deficient offspring; with self-fertilization this danger would become infinitely more serious. Cross-fertilization is the principal rule throughout the whole of Nature, and so it comes about that with hermaphrodites also two individuals are nearly always necessary for propagation. This has the result, however, that the different phases of sexual life, as we know them where the sexes are separate, are again met with here.

There is only one difference, that by and large hermaphrodites are found only among the lower animals: in worms and in snails. They are not found in any of the arthropods or among vertebrates, apart from a very few exceptions among fishes.

A seeming exception to the law of cross-breeding is found in tape-worms. Obviously it is very rare for a host to harbour more than one tapeworm and hence in them cross-breeding is impossible. It is, however, doubtful whether one can speak of a self-fertilization. The tapeworm is an exceedingly remarkable animal. Behind the head comes a short section of neck and then there is a large number of segments or proglottids of which the foremost are the youngest and the rear ones the oldest. Each segment contains a complete hermaphroditic sexual apparatus, so that a single tapeworm possesses hundreds of such equip-ments. According to the current text-book definition the tapeworm is a single entity in which only a multiplication of organs has taken place. Since the foremost segments, which are at first male, mate with the rear ones, which have become female, one should in this case speak of a pure self-fertilization. The tapeworm can, however, with reason be regarded as an animal stock which begets at its hinder end a large number of independent forms of life, the proglottids, by budding. This idea is supported by the fact that there are tapeworms in which the proglottids become quite free inside the host to live there for a long time and in this condition to mate reciprocally. Obviously the odium of incest persists here also, but in any case it would no longer be a pure self-fertilization.

Tapeworms are a clear example of one-sided or self-mating, such that one segment shows male and the other one female behaviour. This may be expected wherever the so-called protandrous hermaphroditism exists, in which the development of the germinal glands does not take place simultaneously, but successively, first a male followed by a female.

This sort of thing is common also in the snails, which are much more advanced. In the hermaphroditic sea-snail (*Acera bullata*), a gastropod, the shell is enclosed within two large fleshy lobes called parapodial lobes. Those sea-snails which are at that moment female show it by lifting the right parapodial lobe, beneath which lies the vaginal opening. Those which are in the male phase now seek to enter the lifted fold of this lobe and insert the penis into this opening by a twist of the fore-body. All in all, these animals behave precisely as if the one were a true male and the other a true female. There can be seen a difference, however, because chains of more than two animals are formed. An approaching third creature with male tendencies may behave towards the second precisely as the second did towards the first. In a chain of this sort, then, which may comprise five or six individuals, only the foremost functions purely as a female, the last only as a male, whilst those between tend in the main towards male propensities yet function as both male and female at one and the same time.

Another very typical example may be mentioned because the chains so formed are particularly remarkable. The American slipper limpet

Fig. 44. Tower building by the slipper limpet (*Crepidula fornicata*). The lowest is female, the upper male. The intervening are in course of turning into females.

(*Crepidula*), which has recently penetrated into European waters, after a certain age leads a sedentary life, since it is nourished by food which drifts by, as are the mussels. Occasionally one finds veritable towers formed by a whole number of these snails perched one on top of the other. Dissection of the limpets forming such a tower always shows that the largest snail, at the bottom, is purely a female and the upper one is recognizable by his well-developed penis as a male. The middle ones show every stage of transition. They are, however, more female the lower their position.

In some pulmonate or lung-breathing snails such unilateral mating may also be observed; in them the "ardent" animal behaves like a male throughout. In the ramshorn snail (*Planorbis carinatus*) the animal in question creeps round the shell of his mate until she takes up a certain position. The penis is now protruded and the male feels round until he has found the female genital opening. The other animal remains quite passive during all this and continues quietly to feed. It may also happen that she rises to the surface to breathe in the middle of it.

Throughout the whole year the earthworm lives entirely by itself and takes no notice whatever of any other member of its kind. When, however, about March the early spring sunshine warms the soil a little, then the mature worms feel that urge which cannot be denied to unite with others. To see this one must of course get up very early in the morning and visit a suitable spot. One can then make the striking observation that the earthworms have all emerged from their holes and are lying with the fore-parts of their bodies across each other in pairs. Unfortunately, we know only the fact and nothing else. We do not know what impulses they arouse in each other. They cannot see. It may be the sense of smell or perhaps of touch which draws them together. Moreover, it is difficult to comprehend how they find the proper position relative to each other. Fig. 45 shows that each earthworm has, approximately from the thirtieth segment onward, a wide belt in which the skin is much thicker and more glandular than in the rest of the body. This is the so-called clitellum. The worms, then, lie on top of each other in such a way that the clitellum of one animal adheres to the fore-region of the other, not very firmly, for an approaching human footstep will drive the two animals apart to disappear in their tunnels, but firmly enough for the act of reciprocal mating. From the male genital opening of each worm issues a small quantity of seminal fluid which is transported to the rear, that is towards the head of the other

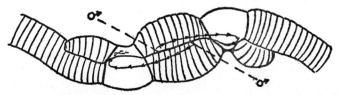

Fig. 45. Mating position of earthworm. The arrows indicate the course of the seminal groove in which the semen is transferred to the receptaculum semenalis of the other.

worm, by a groove in the skin. The semen flows to a point where lie the spherical bladders opening outwardly. These are the so-called receptacula seminalis, their task being to receive the seminal fluid. As soon as this has occurred both worms are satisfied and separate, to relapse for another year into complete indifference to each other. As we have seen, in this act no fertilization of the eggs has taken place. This happens very much later when each worm sets to work, in the bosom of the earth, to deposit its eggs. It then fashions a cocoon with the help of the glands of its clitellum and then starts backing out of it. Whilst doing this it leaves a number of eggs and some seminal fluid behind it in the cocoon and then withdraws from it entirely. The elastic cocoon closes up both in front and behind and the embryo can develop inside it undisturbed. For only one young worm is, in fact, hatched from each such cocoon. Its brothers and sisters have served as nourishment for it.

Matters are more complicated in the roman snails, where true flirtation may be observed. The peculiar behaviour of these animals had already attracted the attention of naturalists in the seventeenth century. The first phases we, unfortunately, do not know. Roman snails, also, do not live so close together in a natural state that they can meet by chance. The ardent animals must therefore seek each other out, but how this comes about is wholly unknown. When two of them have found each other a curious set of preliminaries begins directly (see Plate VI). The snails raise themselves, press the soles of their "feet" firmly together and each tries to lay the right side of its neck against the neck of the other, where the genital opening lies. Before actual mating occurs a characteristic preliminary takes place. This particular snail possesses a very remarkable organ, the so-called "love-dart". This is a pointed, hard, limy rod, lodged in a special bag, the love-dart sac. The love-dart is now plunged into the mate's body with great violence, usually into the edge of the foot. Since we cannot gauge the feelings of animals we will never be able to tell what this procedure means. It is generally accepted that by this act the sexual excitement of the animals is increased, because only after the mutual dart-plunging does the urge for mating awake fully. Only now do they start to cross heads, to extrude the very large penis and to insert it into the female genital opening of the other. As a rule, this is successful only after some time.

PART TWO

The Care of the Young

12

EGG-LAYING

THE begetting of progeny is the last and most profound meaning of the entire sexual life. Everything that we have learnt in the first part of this little book, from the wedding garment to the courtship period, is calculated and shaped to this end. In many of the lower animals, such as the sea-urchin, the play is ended with the ejection into the open sea of the ova and the spermatozoa. The eggs are fertilized and progeny is prepared for its entrance into the new life. They no longer need their parents, but develop by means of their own strength into larvæ which float about in the boundless sea and feed themselves, or else into embryos inside the protective shell of the eggs. These animals stand in contrast, nevertheless, to a large number of species to which the care of their broods is one of the most essential parts of their lives; and with the life and behaviour of these we will concern ourselves in this second part of the book. Here we must assume that care of the young is in no way a peculiarity of the higher animals, in whom one may presume some physical capacity to that end. In fact this same capacity is found in nearly all groups of the metazoa from the sponges, which stand at the lowest threshold of the animal kingdom, upward.

(*a*) DEPOSITION IN FAVOURABLE PLACES

The simplest form in which the care of the mother for her brood is seen is in the correct deposition of her eggs. Every egg-laying animal has the infallible instinct to deposit the eggs only where the progeny may develop undisturbed and under the best conditions. Innumerable examples point to this.

For many eggs which are deposited externally without protecting shells, a certain amount of moisture is indispensable; conditions must be neither too dry nor too damp. The soil offers the best guarantees for this, and therefore it is customary for many different animals to lay their eggs in the damp earth. This is done by, to name only a few, land snails, many insects and a number of spiders. These are all animals whose young hatch out of the egg complete and are instantly ready to fend for themselves by going only a short distance to find their first food. In many cases a convenient hollow is used, in others one is constructed. Among the vertebrates there are many reptiles which belong to this class; the majority of lizards and tortoises as well as many snakes bury their eggs in the moist earth. Humidity plays an important

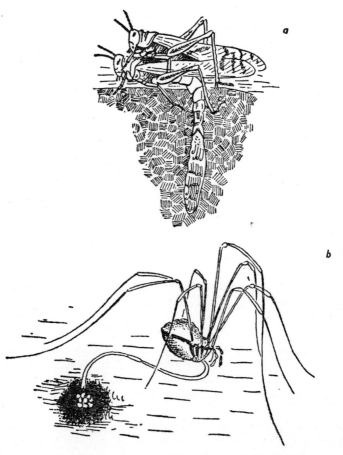

FIG. 46. Depositing ova in the earth: (a) grasshopper; (b) daddy long-legs.

part with these eggs, because unlike birds' eggs they do not possess a firm shell. There is therefore great danger that they may either go mouldy or dry up. It is just in this that the art of the mother consists, to find a really favourable spot. Another art which is thoroughly understood is that of covering the site so skilfully that no trace remains visible and it is made difficult for nest robbers to discover it.

A few animals have learnt to be even more cunning. Their instinct tells them that besides the correct moisture a measure of warmth is required for development to proceed, and that within certain limits the higher the temperature to which the delicate embryos in their shells are exposed the more quickly will they develop. They therefore look about for an incubator, and after some trouble they discover it where decaying vegetation has collected in some corner. In some such heap they then hide their eggs. Man has been very helpful to the habits of these animals, to which our ringed snake belongs, by making compost heaps or piling up tan or sawdust, and so on, in his yard. In a heap such as that the adder seeks a depression, places her cloaca opening over it, raises her tail high and allows the eggs to drop into the pit.

All these animals take what they find without altering it. The brush turkeys alone have taken an immense step forward and have become real technicians. One of them, *Lipoa ocellata*, has in consequence earned the name of the thermometer bird. This bird, which lives in Southern Australia, makes a circular pit, about two feet wide and one foot deep,

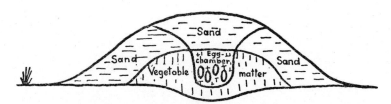

FIG. 47. Diagrammatic cross-section through the nesting mound of a brush turkey, *Lipoa ocellata*.

at some convenient place in the bush. The sand scratched out is thrown up into a mound. Apparently both parents join in this great work. Into this pit they pile all sorts of vegetable matter, chiefly, no doubt, dry leaves but also bits of bark and so on. When the pit has been filled the wise birds allow the hollow to remain open for four to five months.

Since this is during the rainy season the stuff is nicely moistened. Six to nine days before the hen-bird starts to lay she makes a hole, of considerable depth and width, in the middle of the vegetable matter. This will be the egg chamber. The sides of this egg chamber consist of solid material into which twigs, grass stalks and leaves are woven. Then the eggs are laid in it and in such a manner that they do not touch each other. Finally the egg chamber is covered again with the scratched-out herbage and the whole covered with the heaped-up sand into a huge hillock which is quite three foot high and four to six feet in diameter. The whole operation takes about a month. However, the bird then spares itself the task of brooding, for when the eggs are deposited the parent birds go their separate ways. When the young brush turkey chicken, which is hatched by the heat from the decaying vegetation, emerges after some forty-five days it rapidly digs its way to the surface, has a good look round, shakes itself and runs straight into the bush, never having known its parents.

A most peculiar way of sheltering their eggs, which has indeed brought them into disrepute as parasitic brooders, is exercised by bitterling (*Rhodeus amarus*), small lively inhabitants of the fresh waters of Europe. The female has a long ovipositor (Fig. 48), which shows that the animal is up to something unusual. Throughout the year this tube is fairly short. With the coming of spring and with it the spawning season the tube grows to its full length in a few days, under the influence of the sex hormones. A pair of bitterling now have the astonishing instinct to seek one of the large mussels lying on the bottom.

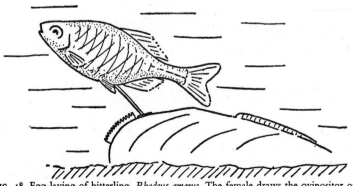

FIG. 48. Egg-laying of bitterling, *Rhodeus amarus*. The female draws the ovipositor out of the siphon opening.

The female inserts her long tube with great caution into the widely opened inhalant siphon, an oval opening lying at the rear and through which the mussel takes in the water which brings the food and the necessary oxygen into the body. The female bitterling now squirts a quantity of unfertilized eggs into the siphon, and these then make their own way to the gill cavity. When this bold act has succeeded it is the male's turn and he pours his semen into the same place so that fertilization is assured. The embryos are found later well concealed in the gill of the mussel. It was formerly believed that a true parasitism was present here and that the embryos were nourished by the juices of the mussel. Today we know that the embryos feed on their own yolk until hatched and only use the mussel as a safe harbourage.

(b) BROOD PARASITES

Brood parasites allow their offspring to be reared by others. There would be no objection to this did they not use very cunning and even abominable methods. The best-known example is the cuckoo. This remarkable bird has completely lost the instinct to build a nest and itself look after its own progeny. Instead it has developed the astonishing new instinct of placing its eggs in the nests of other birds. These are always small birds, mostly songsters, and each female cuckoo has in this her own special habits. One may prefer the redstart, another the shrike, a third possibly the yellow bunting. But the most astonishing thing is that the cuckoo's eggs have come to resemble the host's to a great extent, both in size and colouring. First, they are much smaller than might be expected in such a large bird, and, secondly, they have in many cases the same colour and markings as the host's eggs. This sounds rather like a fairy-tale, but it is a well-authenticated scientific fact. In Finland, for instance, the eggs of the hosts preferred there are blue and the Finnish cuckoo correspondingly lays blue eggs. In England on the other hand the song birds with which the cuckoo deals have speckled eggs, hence here the cuckoo's eggs are also speckled. Fundamentally it must be so, for otherwise the cuckoo would have little success. But how shall we explain this exceedingly remarkable affair? Some rather naïve researchers have imagined that the cuckoo knows what sort of eggs it lays and looks accordingly for a host nest whose eggs they match. This is easily contradicted by the fact that the female cuckoos frequently make mistakes. This may be observed especially where there are many song birds together which lay different kinds of eggs. It is much more probable that Darwin's principle of natural selection has here again been proved. The cuckoo lays its eggs at random. The more conspicuous ones are cast out by the host birds, the less conspicuous remain. After this proceeding has been going on for some tens of thousands of years only those cuckoo hens have survived which prefer those hosts laying eggs bearing a certain resemblance to her own.

Our crime story, however, goes very much farther. First we will make a comparison. When in the close circle of the family or in some

FIG. 49. Cuckoo, *Cuculus canorus*. Nestling about fifty hours old in the act of casting overboard one of its host's eggs.

other not too big community there is a person with thievish propensities directed towards purses of money, this fellow will often attempt to cover up his tracks by the following trick. He takes two half-crowns from the purse and substitutes two shillings for them. The number of coins remains the same, and possibly the cheated person may not even notice that he has been lightened by that little. Mrs. Cuckoo does exactly the same. Very often, if not always, she removes one of her host's eggs before laying hers in the nest. Even though the rightful owner has certainly not counted her eggs, the optical impression of the lay-out is thus preserved. But even this trick would be of no use were not the instincts of the young cuckoo congenial to those of the mother's as soon as it hatches out. It is a born criminal. It is still blind and stark naked and quite incapable of feeding itself. But in its bosom the murderous urge has already awakened to do away with all its step-brothers and -sisters and to become the sole owner of the nest (see Fig. 49). Following its blind urge it loads one egg (or chick) after another on its back, steadies it there with its wings and slides it gradually up to the edge of the nest, by means of the unassisted movement of its legs. Thence it throws the egg overboard. Soon it is alone, and one would think that now the monstrously deceived mother on her return home would at last notice what had happened to her brood. But she notices nothing at all. Birds are creatures of instinct, and no intellect can be observed in them apart from a few exceptions. When the eggs are hatched the mother bird has only one urge, to feed her young. She does not see that suddenly but one remains in the nest whereas before there were five. She does not see that one of her own brood lies dying on the edge of the nest and she feeds the forever hungry murderer of her own children with exemplary perseverance and endless diligence (see Plate XXI).

Cuckoos are distributed over a large part of the world, and nearly everywhere they carry on the same game. Where they do not they have acquired other peculiar habits. In South American cuckoos (*Crotophaga ani*) the females practise a kind of nest communism. These birds live communally and always appear in so-called flights. The females of one of these flights find it more comfortable to arrange a common nest for themselves in which they all deposit their eggs. How in these circumstances the hatching and other affairs are regulated does not seem to be known yet.

Besides cuckoos there are all over the world numerous other families which have hit upon the same artifices as the cuckoo. In South America there are certain starlings, in the Old World some weaver birds, some honey-guides and others. The naturalist is surprised that the adaptations in all these birds are very similar to the cuckoo's. Everywhere, it seems, the eggs resemble in colour the host's own, everywhere a part of the host's brood is destroyed to make way for their own. In some of these nest parasites a similarity has developed, in time, between the young hosts' chicks and the parasites. The adult brood parasite may perhaps have quite a long tail, like a magpie, and in other ways also look quite different to the host. The young parasite, however, has, until it is fledged, that is to say as long as it is under the care of his involuntary foster-mother, a most deceptive likeness to its host (see Fig. 50).

In insects also there are various kinds that behave like the cuckoo. Cuckoo bees, whose best-known species is the *nomada*, are very clever at laying their eggs in the cells of other bees, especially of *Andrena*. They observe exactly where an *Andrena* builds its nest. When the ndustrious little bee has carried the necessary stores of nourishment into the individual cells and perhaps goes off on a final foray, then the parasite bee, which has lurked in the vicinity, pops quickly in and lays an egg in each cell. Nothing further is required. When the female *Andrena* later also lays her eggs, the larvæ of the parasite grow quicker and devour the entire store of food so that the rightful owners perish.

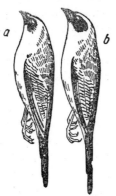

FIG. 50. Widow birds (*Vidua*): (*a*) young brood parasite; (*b*) adult host-bird.

The parasitic humble-bee (*Psithyrus*), which parasitizes various other humble-bees, does it in much the same way. She facilitates her affairs by allowing herself to be adopted into the humble-bee's nest in the spring. Then she can fly in and out of the nest unharmed and in addition feed on her host's honey. She does not lay in all the cells but only a portion of them and thus host and parasite get on quite well together. On the other hand two *Psithyrus* females cannot tolerate each other in the same nest and one of them must leave.

Finally, we must note that there is also a cuckoo weevil among the beetles. The oak gall weevil understands how to roll up an oak-leaf in an artistic manner and to lay an egg in the resulting parcel. The funnel roller weevil (*Rhynchites sericeus*) does not go to all this trouble; why should she? It is much simpler to wait until a roll has been made and to smuggle an egg in quickly or to bore a hole in the completed envelope and pop an egg in.

(c) INVERTED HABITS

Man despairs if he has to conform to a tradition of a couple of hundred years which, so he believes, weighs him down intolerably. He sighs with Goethe: "Woe to you that are a grandson." The animals on the other hand must in their behaviour accord with things which may have been reckoned as well justified millions of years ago yet nowadays bear the stigma of the grossest backwardness.

The toad lives entirely on land exactly like the field mouse which she frequently meets on her nightly peregrinations, and a tree frog feels just as much at home in a wood of green foliage as does the twittering bird. When, however, spring comes both must hop to the nearest pool, there to spawn. Why must this happen? Many million years ago the

PLATE XXI.
Blackcap, feeding a young cuckoo.

PLATE XXII.
Whitethroat, feeding its young.

forebears of our amphibians spent all their lives in water. The adults meanwhile gradually adapted themselves to a life on land, but the young have not yet achieved this new mode of life.

In reptiles we meet the same law. The large turtles, the hawksbill turtles which supply ladies with their beautiful tortoise-shell, and the mighty green turtles which must sacrifice their lives for the sake of gourmets, are as much at home on the high seas as are fish or whales. But for their procreation they must follow their obscure urges and seek out a sandy shore. There, where they are persecuted barbarously by man, they lay their hundreds of eggs in the white sand. This also they do only because their ancestors in earlier ages lived wholly on land. In the interval the adult animals have acquired true flippers, have become fish-eaters and disport themselves in the open sea, but their propagating customs have never been given up. Without doubt they will in consequence be destroyed, for man will extirpate them.

(d) LAYING THE EGGS ON APPROPRIATE FOOD

Herbivores

The remarkable habit of depositing the eggs immediately upon the food needed by the future larvæ or young has been developed in a single group of animals only, namely insects. This may be correlated with the fact that such a proceeding is possible only in very small animals for which the natural food of the creatures is found in quantities much greater than the animal itself, so that it has abundant food for its entire lifetime. Among insects we will first examine vegetable-feeders, in which matters are simple.

Let us commence with the butterflies. Here the females of the great majority have the same instinct, to deposit the eggs on the plant which nourishes the caterpillar. This is necessary, for the caterpillars of many species are monophagous, that is to say they eat only the leaves of a single variety of plant or of only a very few plants and would rather die of hunger than eat anything else. How does the mother pick the right plant out of a multitude of others? First it must certainly be presumed that she has a hereditary knowledge of the smell of the food plant. This seems simple, for the innate knowledge of such characteristics is already known to us. Nevertheless there are complications in this case, at least for the naturalist. The beautiful caterpillar of the privet hawk-moth is found for example on three different plants—lilac, privet and ash. This seems at first wonderful, but there is a simple answer when we find that

6—LLA

these three plants which look so different belong to the same family, the oleaceas. The rest must, however, be guessed. It is extremely likely that privet, lilac and ash produce a certain volatile oil which attracts the female moth or butterfly. We are more precisely informed about other butterflies.

The caterpillar of *Papilio ajax* is found on eighteen different umbellifers, which produce various volatile oils. It has, however, been found that they all contain a certain substance, methylnonylketon, and

FIG. 51. Spanish dung beetle, *Copris hispanica*. Female in the brood chamber with her four dung-pears.

it is obviously this which leads the female to the correct plant. It may therefore be seen that the sensory organs of insects play the most outstanding part in these instincts. Not only, however, is the sense of smell, of which we shall learn more later, important but other senses may also be concerned. Thus the blue-green colour of a cabbage leaf becomes a magnet for the female of the cabbage-white butterfly at the time of egg-laying, whereas during the first days of her life as a butterfly, when her sole desire is to sip nectar, only the bright colours of flowers have any message for her.

The dung beetles, which we may also class as vegetarians, are in a much more difficult position than the leaf-eaters. They cannot lay their eggs just like that, in dung in the street, for it will be dry in a few days and unserviceable as food for the larvæ. They are therefore compelled to bury the dung and also to make some other arrangements. In this respect each species has its own special ways. Our dung beetles have a comparatively easy time. If on some forest path they come across some, for them, deliciously scented horse droppings they creep inside and thence make a deep vertical passage into the earth, with various egg-chambers. The passages are stuffed full of dung and everything will now proceed according to plan.

Some Southern European species which usually have to deal with sheep or goat dung have more quaint habits. The pill-roller scarab beetles, which were already known to the ancient Egyptians, are famous. They can frequently be seen transporting the ball of collected dung over long distances with much labour, either alone or in company with another, until they reach the burrow in which their brood may be successfully reared.

In Spanish dung beetles (*Copris hispanica*) both parents take part in the care of the brood. Having found a heap of sheep's dung they construct under it a large vault, smoothing its walls with great care. This by itself is an enormous labour, for the masses of earth which they must get rid of, up through a narrow tunnel, are many hundred times the weight of their own bodies. Then the dung is transferred to this chamber, and first formed into a large cake by the female, now working alone. From this she cuts four pear-shaped lumps of dung and at the narrow end of each she lays an egg. The female remains faithfully by the eggs, and in doing so probably performs a very important task. The dung would certainly grow mouldy were the mother not continuously busy cleaning its surface. It may be conjectured that she does this by eating the mould. In lunar dung beetles (*Copris lunaris*) eight such dung-pears are constructed, and the male also remains faithfully by the side of the female. When the period of development is at last over and the eight young beetles hatch out, the entire family flies together into the open one fine day. Now, however, family life has come to an end, for each pursues its own path.

Carnivores

We will now briefly consider the meat-eaters. Among bluebottles matters are at their simplest. As every housewife knows, the longish white eggs may be readily detected on meat if it is left uncovered for any length of time in summer. The delicate smell of fresh meat, or better still the stench of decay, attracts these animals with irresistible force. It is the same with a large number of flies. At the same time, it also leads to their undoing. Insectivorous plants set their cunning trap by using the flies' appetite for strong-smelling animal substances as a lure.

The ichneumon flies inject their egg or eggs, by means of their long ovipositors, directly into the interior of the host animal. The larvæ hatching out live in plenty, on the "fleshpots of Egypt", so to speak. They grow quickly and, when ready to pupate, they bore through the

FIG. 52. Hawk-moth caterpillar with the cocoons of ichneumon fly. The larvæ ripe for pupating have bored through the skin.

skin of their host to spin their cocoons in the open. As long as the host animal carries these unpleasant parasites inside it one can, as a rule, see nothing wrong with it. The expert, it is true, may see one or more black spots on the infected caterpillar. These are the points of ingress. At the same time the caterpillars also show a certain discoloration. Otherwise they behave quite normally. Above all they develop an enormous appetite and are generally larger than their normal brothers and sisters. This is not surprising, because they have to eat not only for themselves but also to sustain all their tenants. As soon, however, as their grown-up parasites have bored their way out, the life of the host is finished. The caterpillar collapses like an empty balloon and shortly is as dead as a doornail.

The question has often been raised how it comes about that the host animals do not die much sooner. If we dare to formulate the frightful thought of how we ourselves would fare if in our insides we had a number of correspondingly large parasites to carry about, to eat away happily and destroy all our organs, we should have the answer: we would die in a few days. It is therefore obvious that the ichneumon fly larvæ in the insect body do not attack the vital organs, the nervous system, the heart and so on. They confine their attentions rather to the adipose body. The caterpillar does not require this massive organ lying between the skin and the gut for its own use and therefore it does not matter if the parasites devour it. The adipose body is needed only when it comes to building up the organs of the mature insect inside the pupa.

It must be admitted, then, that the ichneumon fly larva proceeds with astonishing wisdom. It does this not by any calculation or with the

Fig. 53. Ichneumon fly, *Rhyssa persuasoria*, in the act of pricking an egg into the larva of ɐ giant wasp (*Sirex gigas*), which is hidden in the wood of the tree.

foreknowledge that it would be digging its own grave if it killed its host prematurely. No special instincts are required to preserve these ways. It probably sticks to the adipose body because that tastes best, and so everything arranges itself neatly.

Ichneumon flies need an astonishingly acute sense of smell.

The large *Rhyssa persuasoria*, common in pine forests, attacks the fat larvæ of the giant wasp (*Sirex gigas*). These, however, do not creep about in the open but live concealed deep in the trunks of pines and firs under the bark. Through the bark and intervening wood, the *Rhyssa* must therefore be able to scent the exact position where one of these larvæ is lying.

Even more remarkable is the following, which has only recently been brought to light: with some species of *Rhyssa* a host can harbour a whole lot of parasitic larvæ in its interior, for it has food enough for all. In others the relations between host and parasite are more delicately balanced. The mass of the body of the host just suffices to nourish one parasite; for two it is too small. If therefore two mother *Rhyssas* pierce this host, then both parasites succumb to undernourishment. Such a hyperparasitism must then be avoided and in fact no such double laying is ever found. This proves that the ichneumon fly, before depositing her egg, must know for certain whether the host she has chosen has already been infected or not. But how does she go about this? When one knows, the answer seems quite simple. The first fly has run about over the host when depositing her egg and the second detects the smell of these tiny trails. If the host is thoroughly cleaned with alcohol and well dried then it will be confidently laid in a second time.

A devilish method indeed of feeding their progeny is employed by the hunting wasp (*Ammophila campestris*). These lay their eggs upon the surface of another animal, which they have already paralysed but not killed. The sequence of the instinctive acts, which form a real chain, is illustrated in Fig. 54. First a burrow is dug in which the larva can develop. Then a suitable prey is found, overpowered and paralysed by a prick of the poisonous sting. After this the prey is dragged to the entrance of the cave (*a*). It is, however, not taken in immediately, but only when the cautious wasp is convinced that nothing has been altered in the cave during her absence. In the case illustrated some small stones which had fallen in had to be removed (*b*). Only then will she seize her prey and with great difficulty drag it to its intended position (*c* to *f*). Finally the egg will be deposited on its larder (*g*) and the burrow will be left. The last instinctive act of artistically closing the entrance to the burrow has not been illustrated.

It had been previously assumed that the prey was killed by the sting, since it remained completely motionless. This would hardly be judicious, for it would begin to decay in a few days or would dry up, and the development of the wasp larva takes several weeks. We know now that the sting acts similarly to the notorious poison of the South American Indians, curare. It paralyses the muscles but the heart

continues to beat. In this way the prey remains alive for weeks and has
the doubtful pleasure of being eaten slowly but surely by the larva of
the parasite.

The hunting wasps are often closely specialized to take only certain
animals. Some have specialized in caterpillars, as shown in our illustration, others in certain beetles, others again in spiders. We think we
know today that many of them prey upon one particular species only

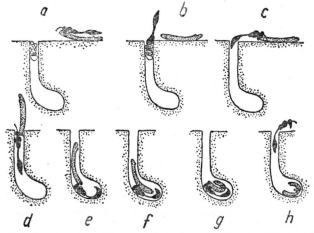

FIG. 54. Hunting wasp, *Ammophila campestris*, placing a paralysed caterpillar in the brood
chamber. In (g) depositing her egg on the caterpillar.

and hunt only that. The prey are often strong and truculent animals
and are overpowered only after a long and grim struggle. This is
especially true of spiders, which are, after all is said, themselves
notorious killers. They are always prepared to attack their prey with
great alacrity, but a free fight, "man to man", in the open is something
they do not understand. The wasp knows quite well how to arrange
matters so that the spider is lured out of its safe stronghold. Then it has
the advantage of the spider because of its mobility and its ability to fly,
and the fight always ends in a victory for the wasp.

13

NOMADIC ANIMALS

MANY animals are unable to breed until they have covered distances which are enormous judged by human standards. This is true of two groups of animals, the migrating fish and the migratory birds. In both cases we are dealing with an historical problem. No logical ground can be adduced for birds flying across half the globe until they eventually find a suitable breeding-place. It is just as illogical that migratory fish should have to traverse thousands of miles through entire river basins and through distant seas for the same purpose. In both cases, fish and fowl, the present situation is one that has been created in times past, and we are no longer in a position to grasp all aspects of this difficult problem.

Let us first consider the fishes.

The most interesting of them is no doubt the eel. Formerly all that was known about it was that it lived in rivers and lakes and that the female could be met with in the upper reaches and the male in the lower reaches or at the mouths of rivers. Absolutely nothing was known of their methods of breeding and it was especially remarkable that spawning eels were never found. This is nowadays still so. No one has ever seen a spawning female, and even spawning males are extremely rare.

A certain amount of light was shed on these very obscure problems when it was noticed that in the spring, on all the coasts of Europe, slender little fish only a few inches in length and as transparent as glass appeared in the sea and gradually ascended the rivers. It was also seen that these fish turned into true young eels, one feature of the change being a very rapid pigmentation of the body. Now at any rate one thing could be guessed; this was that the eel is a migratory fish spawning at sea and in its youth ascending the rivers, passing the greater part of its life there (ten to twelve years), and when mature again descending the river and disappearing into the mysterious depths of the ocean from which it originally emerged. There is, however, no return from these depths; the eel spawns once only in its lifetime and then dies.

The layman may perhaps be satisfied with this information, but for the naturalist the matter only now begins to be really interesting.

There were two questions in particular which clamoured for the attention of anyone who had given it any thought. Where did the eels spawn in the sea? And what did they look like in their earliest stages? for never yet had man found young eels at sea. These would necessarily be smaller than the elvers which appear in spring at the mouths of rivers.

It was therefore a really important discovery when it was found that a deep-sea animal, which had long been known under the name of *leptocephalus* and which looks like a willow leaf in shape and size, is gradually transformed into a young eel. This *leptocephalus* was without doubt the long-sought eel larva, and it only remained for us to find the precise spawning-ground of the eels. This, however, proved to be no trifle. Above all, then, how many spawning-grounds were there actually? Was there a northern and a southern race, or has each of the great European nations a special spawning-ground of its own separated from that of the others?

During many laborious sea voyages occupying many years the famous Danish explorer Johannes Schmidt attempted to solve the problem. He fished the whole Atlantic systematically and everywhere he measured the eel larvæ accurately. The result may be seen in the accompanying chart. Where only quite tiny larvæ, about four-tenths of an inch in length, were found, there approximately must lie the breeding-ground. But this was far away from our shores, in the West Atlantic near the Bermudas. The immense distance from there to the coasts of Europe is covered by these tiny beasts in a constant easterly pilgrimage lasting two years. In the course of this they grow to the comparatively majestic length of two to three inches. In the third year, when already nearing the European continent but still in deep water, the transformation of the *leptocephalus* into the glass-eel occurs during a prolonged fast; and at the beginning of the fourth year the sea voyage is at last completed. There still remains, however, the long, weary journey up the river.

We have taken up far too long a time with the larvæ, but in paying our tribute to their feats we must not forget their elders, whose performance is equally wonderful. The distance covered by the adult eels is some 3,000 nautical miles to the point where they eventually reach their spawning-grounds. How do they find their way in the gloomy depths of the sea? This is likely to remain their secret forever, yet we can find out something about the eel itself. It is the prototype of the good European. There are no English, German or Italian races of eels, but only one single European eel, because all the eels of Europe congregate at the same spawning-ground and there lay the keel of a new generation.

A second group of migratory fish is the salmon, where, however, matters are reversed. This magnificent fish spawns in the upper reaches of rivers, frequently indeed in mountain streams, but spends the greater

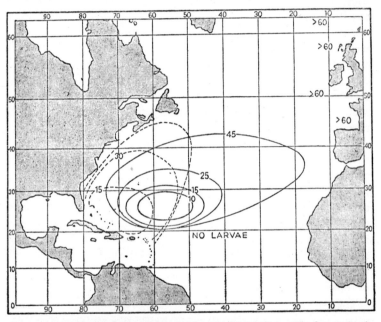

FIG. 55. Spawning-ground of the European eels in the Atlantic Ocean. The figures give the length of the eel larvæ, in millimetres, found within the curve.

part of its life at sea. It is true that salmon do not as a rule depart very far from their home waters, but a hundred miles means nothing to them. For the young fish following its instinct, to swim downstream until it reaches the sea can hardly be regarded as much of an effort, since the current does most of the work of carrying it seaward. Moreover, these little creatures often muster in schools in which one leads and the remainder follow. All the same, as we shall see, the young fish must be careful during their river passage to notice the characteristics of their native place. In the sea they grow rapidly; some species ascend their river annually, others again do so once only in their lifetime, to spawn and then expire.

During this long journey, made against the stream, the fish shows what it can do. In the first place, speaking in purely physical terms, this voyage is a tremendous feat. In the higher reaches of the river there are rapids and small waterfalls which would prove impassable barriers for all other fish. Salmon, however, pass over; a mighty leap and away over a rapid measuring several yards provides a splendid picture for any Nature-lover. It is, nevertheless, a far greater achievement that the animals should know exactly whence they came. This most remarkable fact was firmly established only when the marking of young salmon before their journey to the sea had been undertaken. After a few years it became apparent that the same individuals found their way with great regularity to the place where they had first seen the light of day. We still do not know how it is done, for the ramifications of some of these river systems are numberless and at every fork the salmon must take an important decision. We also do not know why it should matter so much to them to return to their birthplace, but for the fisheries the fact that they do is of the greatest value. When a dam is constructed a hundred and fifty or more feet high even the boldest salmon-leap comes to nought. He does not, however, turn to a neighbouring branch of the river to try his luck, but struggles in front of the obstacle until he dies. Thus all the spawning fish must be captured and carefully carried to another stream. There artificial insemination is carried out and then the young fish are provided with a new home to which they may find their way back unhindered by the work of man.

The second group of migrants, the universally known birds of passage, will not occupy us for long, since an extensive literature exists on this subject and most of it may be taken for granted. Everyone knows that storks go south in the autumn and that they get as far as South Africa. Each one of us bids a sad farewell to the swallows, whose departure heralds the autumn. In one respect all migratory birds in the northern hemisphere are alike; they breed in the north and wander south before the beginning of the winter. That they do this latter cannot be held against them. Many of us would gladly follow their example and spend the winter in the sunny south. That the migrant birds are avoiding the winter cold is demonstrable, for in countries that have a severe winter the proportion of birds which fly south is greater than in those with a mild winter climate. But there is a further question:

Why do the birds not remain the whole year in the far south and for what reason do they feel the irresistible urge in the spring to return across the wide seas and over hill and dale to the north? This habit cannot be an ancient inheritance, for in the glacial period, some 10,000 years ago, the whole of Northern Europe was buried under snow and ice and did not afford a suitable breeding-ground. The migratory birds, then, have acquired their remarkable behaviour in more recent times only. A key to the understanding of bird migration may be found perhaps in the attentive observation of the life and activities of our birds during the summer. Swallows are tirelessly busy from early morn to dewy eve. Not to be distracted, they pursue their tiny prey and every now and then return to the nest to feed their young. In the tropics they could do at most about twelve hours or so; in the north, on the other hand, the summer days are much longer than the night so that every day they can squeeze in an extra couple of hours or more for feeding their young. Perhaps this is the main meaning of bird migration!

For the rest, it must never be lost sight of that bird migration is an historical problem which has not yet been fully probed. It is probably beyond discovery why some birds travel half-way round the world to rear their young. Some far northern sea-birds fly as far as Hawaii, others from Northern Japan go to Australia. Why? We do not even know why the Goths migrated from their Swedish homeland to Italy 1,500 years ago! How then can we expect to solve the other much more difficult problem?

14

PROTECTION OF THE EGGS BY THE PARENTS

It is an amiable trait found throughout the whole animal kingdom that many parents protect their brood with their own lives. Even in the common jellyfish (*Aurelia aurita*) the larvæ remain attached to the underside of the mother. This is perhaps hardly pertinent here, because it can scarcely be an instinctive act on the part of the mother. Care of the brood, in some form or other, is found moreover even in worms. In the Echinodermata also, for instance in starfish and brittle-stars, this phenomenon is frequent. In what follows, we will however concern ourselves chiefly with arthropods and vertebrates.

The simplest form is the guarding of the eggs after they are laid. Animals with serpentine bodies are given to coiling themselves round the spherical egg-masses and thus protecting them. Fig. 56(b) shows how the poisonous *Scolopendra* satisfies her maternal instinct. Her thread-like relatives, the millipedes, which one finds so frequently in damp soil when digging in the garden in spring, behave in exactly the same way. It is interesting to know that true snakes frequently do precisely the

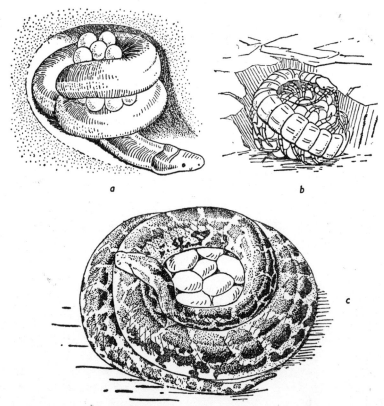

a   *b*

c

Fig. 56. Mothers guarding their eggs: (a) cæcilian, *Ichthyophis glutinosus*; (b) centipede *Scolopendra cingulata*; (c) giant python, *Python molurus*.

same, as is shown in a picture of the enormous Malay python. The idyll does not cease with that, for after the young are hatched they do indeed creep away from the mother, but for the first few evenings each returns to its own eggshell. The cæcilians or blindworms, a specialized group of amphibians, behave similarly. In a deciduous wood in the spring we may often see running about on the ground large numbers of the well-known wolf spiders, of which many are dragging behind them white or coloured little balls. Such balls are cocoons of spun silk which contain the eggs laid by the female. Some weeks later in many species the abdomen is no longer smooth, but has come to look like a blackberry (see Plate XX). This peculiar appearance comes about

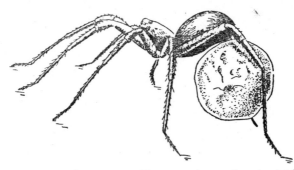

FIG. 57. Wolf spider with egg-cocoon. The cocoon is secured to the abdomen with silken filaments.

because all the young hatched out of the cocoon have now made themselves at home on the mother's abdomen. They sit there closely packed and only if they are disturbed can we see that they are a mass of small living animals, for then they disperse with great rapidity in all directions. Female scorpions frequently take their young for a walk on their backs. In Southern Europe if one turns over a stone in the autumn it is often possible to admire such a family idyll. On the back of the black mother there will be eight or ten, at times even twenty or more, closely packed snow-white little scorpions.

Generally the females of the decapod crustaceans carry their eggs and embryos about with them. These include the fresh-water crayfish, the lobster, some crabs and many more. The eggs when laid are secured by a cement to the swimming legs or the abdomen, which are covered with long filaments, and in this manner they can carry a large mass of eggs about for a long time. Feeding is not interfered with as it is in the cases of snakes that guard their eggs, but probably they have to be a little careful to see they do not become too corpulent. For as long as they carry the mass of eggs they must not shed their skins, since in doing so the shedding of the skin from the legs would also strip off the eggs. Hence it is that at a more mature age the males continue to shed their skins annually, whereas the females always skip the year in which they are carrying eggs and only do so every second year. For the same reason the adult male river crayfish casts his skin twice a year, the female once only.

Many other crustaceans have similar habits. Thus the spider crabs carry their egg-masses with their mouth parts.

It is worth remarking that this habit of carrying the eggs about, common to all other arthropods, seems to be almost entirely absent in insects. Obviously this is correlated with the ability to fly. An animal that flies about in the air cannot very well drag all its offspring about with it all the time. This would be altogether too much of a burden during flight. Only in the bugs which do not fly readily do we know of a few examples in which the eggs are attached to the back. Moreover, in these the male shares this burden.

In vertebrates the carrying of eggs in this manner is, in general, rare; nevertheless it may be observed in some fish and amphibians. A few words must be said about some little-known exotic species of fishes. The male of a New Guinea fresh-water fish, *Curtus gulliveri*, has on his forehead a bony hook-like process which serves to bear a group of eggs. In a species of chad, *Aspredo lævis*, the eggs are stuck on the abdominal surface of the female on small stalks which carry a sort of cup on their ends. The stalks are said to be traversed by several blood-vessels which divide into capillaries in the cup. Probably the embryos are nourished by blood from the mother.

More remarkable is the behaviour of our native pipefish. In these we find a gradual increase from simple to more complicated conditions. In *Nerophis ophidian* the female plasters the flat abdominal surface of the male with eggs, which are attached with a cement-like substance. There is no sort of pouch formed.

Pipefishes are even slenderer than eels; they look like blades of grass and inhabit the beds of sea-grass which extend along some coasts for miles. In all species the female is endowed with an instinct to plant the eggs direct upon the male's abdomen during mating. In the simplest case the surface of the abdomen is not specially modified to that end; at most it is merely somewhat flattened. The firmly cemented eggs form a plate there. In *Syngnathus* the abdominal surface of the male at spawning time shows numerous honeycomb-like depressions with a lip-like rim. In each of these cells an egg is laid and secured with a secretion. The egg-laying takes some days to complete. The lip-like rims now grow rapidly and soon form a true brood-pouch which opens only through a longitudinal slit. Here the embryos develop. Finally, in the sea-horses the male carries a brood-pouch throughout the year, which opens to the exterior only by a small hole. The female must introduce her eggs through this small opening (see Plate XX).

The study of these fish has led us naturally to one of the most remarkable problems in the biology of reproduction, namely to the collaboration of the male in breeding. When animals mate regularly, as do birds, it need not be surprising that the father also takes part in the incubation and in the feeding of the young or any other matters. In some fish, as we find, the peculiar fact is that the female's activity is confined exclusively to the laying of the eggs. Everything else, the transport and care of the eggs, the building of the nest and so on devolves on the male. In frogs, too, there is a similar thing. Even amongst the invertebrates it is not quite unheard of. In the rare sea-spiders or pycnogonids the male is furnished with a special pair of legs, the egg-carriers, to which the egg-masses are attached for transport. These matters have not been explained yet, and their origin during the long course of the earth's history will very likely remain a mystery. That there is no need for the males to be drawn into the nursing is shown by the extreme scarcity of this phenomenon. The care of the brood by the males is therefore obviously the outcome of quite special and fortuitous conditions.

Participation by the males is found also in the so-called mouth-breeders. In a series of fishes there exists the remarkable habit of one of the parents taking the eggs as they are laid into its capacious mouth. Yet it does not swallow them, but cares for them with solicitude until they hatch. The best-known example is in a shad-like fish, *Arius falcarius*. There are, however, not only other shads but representatives of other families, for instance the toothed carp or the cichlids, which exhibit the same instincts. It is the males mainly which undertake this self-sacrificing task. Any feeding by the parent fish during the entire period of hatching is of course out of the question. In *Arius* the œsophagus may even be completely closed during this time, and the entire gut shrinks.

In some fishes this kind of breeding behaviour persists even beyond the embryonic period. In *Tilapia natalensis* it has been observed that the swarm of young fish slip back into the mouth cavity of the parent at the least hint of danger, and that at first the nights also are spent in this well-sheltered space.

Among amphibians there is in Europe a very remarkable species which carries its own eggs on its body. This is the celebrated midwife toad. During mating the male coils the long strings of spawn round his hind legs and they are then secured round his thighs in two large clumps. The further conduct of the male has been somewhat variously described. It was previously assumed that the animal retreated into a

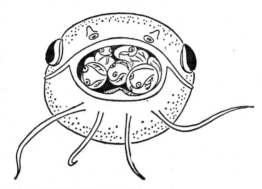

FIG. 58. Male cichlid, *Arius falcarius*, viewed from in front.

hollow in the ground with his egg-masses. Others assert that in spite of his burden he jumps about in a lively manner so that the eggs are continually moistened anew by the dew. During these jaunts the animal may, in certain circumstances, lose a considerable portion of his load. Eggs thus stripped off may indeed develop further, but the tadpoles hatching out naturally perish. For normal development it is essential for the instinct of the male to lead him to enter the water with the egg-masses at the correct moment, there to strip them off (see Plate XX).

Matters are more complicated in certain amphibians which have special breeding spaces or cavities for their progeny. The most remarkable is the Surinam toad (*Pipa americana*) in which the back of the female is used as the breeding organ. When depositing the eggs the female protrudes the oviducts extraordinarily far and is able, possibly with the help of the male, to sprinkle the eggs over the whole surface of her back where they stick fast. Each egg must act as an irritant on the sensitive skin of the back, for growths immediately appear which lead to a high swelling being formed round each. Eventually these all become deep honeycombs, in each of which a small froglet passes its embryonic life. The whole is sealed at the top by a secretion. At the end of the breeding period a lot of hind legs, heads or other bodily parts appear out of the cells, as shown in Fig. 59. True tadpoles do not exist in this species. This is all the more astonishing since the *Pipa*, just like the African clawed toad, spends its whole life in water.

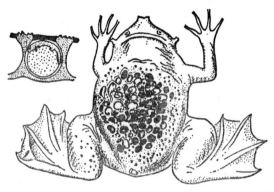

FIG. 59. Surinam toad, *Pipa americana*. Female with brood. On left, section through a dorsa cell with embryo.

Other frogs, such as species of *Nototrema*, have a large breeding sac on their backs which opens to the exterior by means of a longitudinal slit. How the eggs get into this bag seems not to be known. It is worth noting that in this case only a few large eggs are laid as against the hundreds laid by normal frogs. It is evident that there is a great advantage in this method.

15

THE NEST

ANOTHER kind of care for the young consists in the parents preparing a nest in which to deposit the eggs. It is rather difficult to define what exactly is a nest. Let us agree that it is a dwelling with its own walls, in which eggs can be deposited, no matter what the origin of the materials of which it is constructed. There are many such nests through-out the animal kingdom, and all manner of things may be related of them.

(a) NESTS OF INVERTEBRATES

Let us commence with a quite simple case. The small arachnid *Trogulus*, which leads a retiring life under stones, does not itself build a nest but lays its eggs in a small snail-shell and only spins a cover over it. The embryos could desire nothing better. The solid shell protects them from injury and from drying up, the cover prevents the intrusion of predatory animals and is yet sufficiently well ventilated to permit the access of oxygen to the eggs (see Plate XXIII).

Naturally, other methods may be used. The true spiders spin round their spherical egg-masses a cocoon which may equally well be called a nest. Such cocoons must be very familiar to Nature-lovers. Each is a little ball which gives the impression of being fluffy owing to the woolly threads of silk. If we pull it apart it can be seen that it contains a number of tiny eggs. Usually the cocoon is spun between leaves or hidden from sight in some other way; often the mother spider sits close by, and woe to him who disturbs the eggs (see Plate XVII).

In summer one frequently finds, on a blade of grass or flower stem, a so-called fairy lamp, a white bell-shaped structure fastened by a handle. It is an incomplete cocoon of the *Agrœca* spider; the structure is completed by pasting it over with earth (see Fig. 60).

Insects do not go in so much for nest-building. Their eggs are, as a rule, so hard and unyielding that they do not need any particular protection. One such is the great diving beetle (*Hydrous piceus*), which makes a floating nest for its brood usually secured to a leaf floating on the surface of the water and surmounted by a kind of chimney serving as an air-pipe. Réaumur, who not only invented the thermometer but was one of the most eminent naturalists of his time, observed this beetle at work on this remarkable structure. "The walls are parchment-like and the interior is filled with a loose silky webbing. In the foremost part of the cocoon the eggs lie on the floor like a cake nicely stacked in rows alongside one another. The head ends of the eggs are all turned upward; each egg lies in a little silken case, and over the whole egg-cake is spread the finest of fine silk webbing. . . . When the larvæ crawl out the cocoon makes the most lovely nursery. Not particularly roomy, but cosy. Like the gingerbread house in the wood it has the agreeable quality that the children can, at least partially, devour it. The fine webbing round the eggs and that which wedged them in is eaten by the larvæ; even the walls are nibbled at. Only when an exceedingly thin shell remains does the emergence begin, on the rear side under the chimney where the shell is thinnest. The grey larvæ climb up and down the chimney, sunbathe on the upper side of the cocoon or lie in the weeds immediately in front of the door. In the evening or if danger

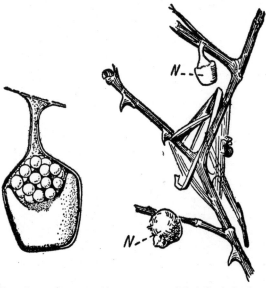

FIG. 60. Spider, *Agroeca brunnea*, with two cocoons (N). (*Above*) An incomplete one; (*below*) completed with earth crust. (*Left*) Section through nest, greatly magnified.

threatens they slip inside. Only after some days do they leave their native hearth for ever" (Wesenberg-Lund).

The greatest architects among the insects are without doubt the Hymenoptera, which include the bees, wasps and humble-bees. From the diversity of structure of their nest a whole science has been built up, and the most varied types of nest have been classified. The pretty nest of our field-wasp *Polistes gallica* is very simple; it may be readily seen in summer, on stones, walls, fences and so on. It is, like that of its relatives, a "gymnodom" or "naked house". This means that the whole nest consists of a few cells only, each containing a grub, but with no protecting wall around them. For the adult wasps therefore such a **nest** offers no shelter. If it is cold or it rains they can at best sit on it and freeze. These animals have, however, already discovered the great mathematical truth of the precise hexagonal cell, which admits of the most complete use of a given space. Individually these gymnodom nests can appear very varied, according to the way the individual combs are put together.

The other wasps' nests may be lumped together as "calyptodom", that is, furnished with a protective outer wall. At first these nests also are, strictly speaking, true breeding establishments, for the progeny only. The wasp founding it in the spring is invariably a fertilized female which has over-wintered. She is entirely dependent on her own devices and has to perform the whole work of construction alone, that is to say

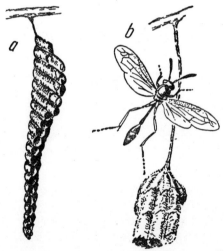

FIG. 61. Simple gymnodom wasps' nests: (*a*) of the *Stenogaster*; (*b*) of the *Myschocyttarus labiatus*.

she must also make the first cells from which later her faithful helpers, the workers, hatch out. With their collaboration, out of the original small nest grows the ever-larger one with thick, many-layered protective wall and with many storeys of superimposed comb. Such a nest ends in being no longer a nest but a community settlement or a government palace in which the whole population from the queen to the youngest worker finds shelter. **Many** a person has found this out to his

cost, when he has come in too close contact with a wasp's nest. All the
inmates burst forth and sting the disturber unmercifully.

The material from which the wasps build their nest is a paper-like
mass which they prepare from wood. Very often in summer one may
see a wasp sitting on a telegraph pole from which it zealously gnaws off
small shavings. The shavings are mixed with saliva to form paper.
Among all these social hymenoptera the care of the young, which in

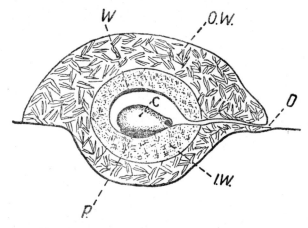

FIG. 62. Nest of humble-bee, somewhat diagrammatic longitudinal section. C. cell, P.
pollen, W. wax layer, I.W. inner wall constructed of moss and leaves, O.W. outer wall,
O. opening.

other animals is borne by the parents, is taken over by the workers or
sterile females. The queen, who provided everything to begin with,
now only lays eggs, and the males also do not do overmuch. The whole
care of the brood from cell-building to feeding the larvæ is transferred
to the workers.

The humble-bee's nest is made quite differently to the wasps' nest
and as a rule is on or in the ground. The founder of the nest is once
again one of last year's females. She first of all digs a small burrow in
some suitable spot and lines it carefully with moss and leaves. The roof
is made impermeable with a layer of wax. The exit from this burrow
is provided by a long tunnel, often measuring half a yard in length. On
the bottom of the nest a piece of so-called bee's bread, an ordinary piece
of pollen mixed with honey, is laid, and above this a hemispherical
waxen cell is built; in this, not one but a round dozen of eggs are

laid. Honey mixed with pollen is also placed at the entrance in a waxen cup (see Fig. 62). The faithful mother watches for several weeks on the roof of the cell until her daughters begin to hatch out, and then she is rewarded for all her trouble, for each of these daughters is an industrious worker with no idle plans for marriage but ready to devote herself wholly to the hive.

We will confine our attention to a few bees only, some of the solitary species, as they are called. It is precisely these little creatures which occasionally make very pretty nests. Many people must have seen in their gardens circular pieces cut out of the leaves of the bushes or trees, which have the appearance of having been cut with a razor-sharp knife. This is the work of the leaf-cutting bees, a species of *Megachile*, which shelter their brood in hollow stalks, tubular stems and so on, and clothe the individual cells, lying one behind the other, neatly with fragments of leaves. Other species use flower petals, shredded plant tissues or finely masticated material for lining their cells. Some bees, species of *Osmia*, regularly shelter their brood in empty snail-shells and complete their cells with chewed plant tissues.

(b) NESTS OF VERTEBRATES
Poikilotherms (cold-blooded animals)

Typical nest structures are made by all sections of the vertebrates. Fish show every transition from the simplest to the most complicated. Salmon make it easy for themselves. When the fish have arrived in the region of mountain streams from their long wanderings in the sea, the female scrapes a pit with her tail and there deposits her eggs, whereupon the male fertilizes them. Thereafter the eggs are carefully covered over with fine gravel. This gravel is sufficiently coarse to allow the passage of oxygenated water, while providing the darkness that favours development. Salmonidæ do not exercise any care over their brood but leave their eggs to look after themselves. Where true nest-making exists it is, on the contrary, always the male that watches over the eggs and ultimately the hatched-out young. A lot of material is not necessarily collected for nest-building. The rockfish or goby (*Gobius minutus*) uses an empty shell. This fish inhabits the inter-tidal zone and can be easily observed at low tide, since the water is then confined to a few shallow pools, in which the fish may be found. The nest-builder is again the male. Having found a suitable shell he will turn it so that the mouth is directed downward. Now the sand underneath the shell is removed with his mouth or sluiced away by fin movements and, finally, the whole shell is covered with sand. In this way a brood cave is created with only a subterranean entrance. When this has been completed the male seeks out a female; she slips into the cave and attaches her eggs to the shell forming the dome of the cave. Since there are apparently fewer males than females in this species, the male fetches one female after another to deposit her eggs.

Some fish build their nests from portions of plants. The wrasse (*Crenilabrus ocellatus*), common in the blue waters of the Adriatic, chooses a variety of threads of seaweed, always with a preference for the green alga *Cladophora*. Here again the male is the sole architect. He tears off the threads of seaweed with his jaws and carries them straight to the nest even from as far as ten yards away; it looks exactly like a bird's nest. Having made it to the requisite size the male fetches a female who deposits her spawn, whereupon he covers the eggs with more threads of seaweed so that they can develop in complete safety in water saturated with oxygen.

The nest of the stickleback, of which very many owners of aquaria will have had personal experience, has achieved the greatest renown. The male first makes a hollow in the sand and then drags every conceivable sort of material to it. In the wild he will use any pieces of vegetation: thread-like algæ, fragments of grass, roots and so on. In the aquarium he has to be content with other materials, such as wool, hair, string and anything else available. The material is forced into the sand and gummed together with a secretion from the kidneys, after which it is sprayed with sand by the mouth. In this way a true nest is gradually built, furnished with a tunnel-like entrance. This entrance is usually marked in some special way, for instance by means of threads of vari-coloured yarn, obviously to make it easier to find again. The rest of his behaviour during breeding is described elsewhere.

An entirely different kind of nest-building is employed by certain tropical fresh-water fishes, especially the paradise fish (macropods), which are nowadays often kept as ornamental fish. They build nests of foam (see Plate XXIII). The foam is made up of air and saliva. The male finds a fair-sized leaf and deposits row upon row of saliva pearls upon it until a voluminous structure of thousands of these arises. The egg-laying then takes place under this nest.

Foam nests are also used by certain tropical amphibians. The source of their materials is different, however, the walls consisting of a

FIG. 63. Foam nest of a frog, *Polypedates rheinwartii*; (*right*) section.

mucus (mucin) from the cloaca of the female converted into foam by rapid movements of her legs. Its use varies. Some species dig themselves into the earth and deposit their eggs, which have been surrounded by the foam, in an artificially constructed cave. Tree frogs, living in trees, fashion such balls of foam between the leaves. While the outer wall is hardening fluid accumulates inside from the bursting of the foam pearls, and in this the tadpoles paddle about as if in a puddle. Probably the foam serves also as their food.

Among reptiles it is mainly the crocodiles that seem to indulge in true nest-building. These saurians either scrape a hole about half a yard deep to bury their eggs, or else cover them with all sorts of vegetable matter. The crocodiles of the Old World seem to prefer the former method. The pits which they scrape with their feet are somewhere between twelve and eighteen inches deep, and the eggs in these are usually found in two tiers divided by a layer of sand. When ready the pits are carefully filled in by the mother and the sand is smoothed off, probably with the tail. The position of the nest is, however, betrayed to those who would like to steal the eggs by a deep furrow left behind in the sand by the mother's tail.

The American alligators go about the business in a somewhat more refined way than their Old World cousins, and make real nests in which reeds and other plants are used. From afar they look like small hay-cocks. Here again the correct choice of position is the mother's principal art. The bottom of the nest is mostly covered with soft leaves or grass stems and is always a little damp. Heat from above and moisture from below seem to be the most important requirements. For the rest, crocodiles are very good mothers. They do not stop short at building a nest, but in many cases also guard it. Above all they assist the little ones to emerge from the egg. Natives have frequently told how, when the time of hatching comes, the mother digs the eggs out. Of this one may be readily convinced, for nests are frequently found in the wild from which the sand has been scraped away. The question now is, how does the mother know that the time has arrived to do so? In this the young help by croaking inside the yet unbroken shell shortly before the time. These sounds, as can be easily ascertained with artificially hatched eggs, are so loud that they can be heard comfortably in an adjacent room, and can be set off by shaking the floor, for instance by walking about with a heavy tread. Crocodiles have excellent hearing and we now also know to what purpose the mother crocodile puts it. She defends her young furiously and stands no nonsense if one disturbs the family life. The explorer Schomburgk has given a very graphic description of this. It refers to an encounter with a Brazilian dusky cayman (*Caiman niger*): "My attention having been attracted by a peculiar cry, very similar to a kitten's. I believed myself to be near the lair of a jaguar, when my companion pointed to the water and called out: 'Young caymans'. The sound issued from beneath the branches of a tree, which had, in consequence of the washing away of the earth round its roots, assumed a horizontal inclination over the water, which it touched with its branches. Cautiously we slid along the trunk as far as the crown, where, below me, I saw the litter of young, each about half a yard long, congregated in the shade. Since we were only about a yard above the surface of the water it was easy for the Indian to transfix one of the young with an arrow and to draw the shrieking, struggling creature out of the water. At that moment a large cayman, the mother, who may have been watching us for some time without our knowledge, came to the surface. She came up below our feet among the twigs, to defend her young, at the same time emitting a hideous roar. . . . Soon the roaring had gathered more caymans under us who stood by the mother faithfully, whilst she raised herself, frequently far more than shoulder high above the water, to tear us down from our position. . . . Every time she was wounded by one of our arrows she withdrew below water for a moment but quickly rose again and renewed her attack with redoubled fury. The water's surface, previously quite still, had turned into a boiling cauldron being continually thrashed by her curving tail, and I must admit that the incredible courage of the animal made my heart beat with doubled speed."

Birds

The best known of all nests is of course the bird's nest, with which we will now deal. Each species builds its nest after its own particular pattern, and it need hardly be mentioned that everything occurs by instinct. With the same certainty with which a spider spins its web or the caterpillar fashions its cocoon, the young bird wishing to found a family for the first time builds its nest in the way prescribed by its ancestry.

The nest structures of birds are of innumerable shapes and forms. In its simplest style the nest has the form of a basin or bowl, out of which the eggs cannot readily fall. In addition the nest offers the brooding bird the necessary support. This most primitive nest has, however, all sorts of disadvantages. It is not only man who knows how nice birds' eggs taste. There are many nest-robbers among animals, and for all these the open nest lying on the ground or in the fork of a tree offers an easy prey. To overcome these handicaps, Nature has taken two different courses. The most elegant solution is afforded by the hanging nest, built by many tropical birds. At a dizzy height at the tip of the branch of a tall tree this nest hangs freely in the air. No four-footed robber dare approach it by climbing. Another construction consists in transposing the opening from above to below, so that one cannot see inside from above. Both types may be combined. Another possibility of sure protection is afforded by building the nest against vertical walls, as do the swallows and martins, for which our towering tenement barracks offer ideal rocky castles. Equally varied can be the material used. The nest is not always prepared from soft vege-table material as is done by our singing birds. Some build their nests of clay, others build them with the help of their own saliva. The so-called edible birds' nests of the swifts in South-Eastern Asia, which consist of saliva only, are well-known examples. Brooding in hollow trees is also much favoured, as by woodpeckers, most parrots, some ducks and many other birds.

Some birds seek to protect themselves and their broods by placing themselves under the care of a powerful overlord with whom none

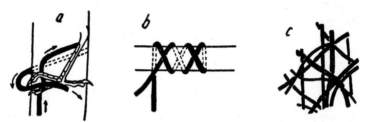

FIG. 64. Weaving skill in nest-building among birds: (a) weaver birds, *Quelea quelea*, with the assistance of their feet; (b) weave of an American starling (icterid); (c) structure of the wall of an icterid's nest.

willingly falls out. One of the most remarkable of these cases is the settling of many songsters in the neighbourhood of the eyrie of a large bird of prey. This would seem at first sight to be a somewhat question-able protection, but is explained by the equally remarkable instincts of the large birds of prey not to hunt near their own eyrie. There exists here then a kind of sanctuary inside which "stronghold peace" reigns, and this has been made use of by the small birds. In this we see how the breeding instincts of one bird may fit in with those of another in a wonderful manner. The protection may, however, be of an altogether different class. In the tropics there exist some song-birds which always build their nests in the vicinity of an exceedingly aggressive species of wasp.

The art of building a nest by no means consists only of putting together the collected material in a certain way. Even among our reed-warblers, which suspend their nest between a few swaying reeds in impenetrable reed forests, we can admire some real basketwork. The celebrated weaver birds of the tropics have gone even further, as they are able to make their knots with the assistance of both their feet and beak to convert the fibres they use into really ornamental fabrics (Fig. 64).

Numerous birds make no nests at all but are content to lay their eggs on the ground in a suitable spot, at most scraping it out a little. This method is particularly practised by our sea-birds: terns, gulls, oyster-catchers and so on. Nature helps them in another way. The eggs of these birds, because of the speckling, harmonize particularly well with their background, so that although they lie quite in the open they are exceedingly difficult to detect. Their peculiar shape prevents them being rolled away by the wind. They are not oval like a hen's egg, but are pear-shaped, so that if they move they turn about their own pointed end and merely roll in circles where they lie. Many large exotic birds behave similarly in that they also build no true nests: the African ostrich, the nandoo, some bustards and some vultures. The guillemots lay their eggs without any nest-building on the terrace-like ledges of precipitous rock cliffs. A more general habit is that of sheltering the clutch of eggs at the end of a long passage dug in the earth. This is found in some ducks (*Casarca*, *Tadorna*, etc.), in the remarkable rabbit-owl (*Speotyto cunicularia*), whose passages may reach a length of two yards, the sand-martin, and many others. The use of existing hollows in trees is favoured by many owls and parrots and also by some pigeons, ducks, song-birds and others.

In nest-building birds use a division of labour similar to that used in incubation. Where a true mating exists, both parents as a rule share in it equally. Nevertheless an interesting sharing of work is still shown. The male takes care of the rough work by providing the materials, and the actual building devolves on the female. This is the way in which the stork and grey heron, among others, carry on. In some species, even so, nest-building has been taken over almost entirely, or completely, by one sex. In the greenfinch the female builds alone, while in the rook the female does most of the work. In yet other species the male appears to be the sole architect. It has recently been shown for the Savi's warbler (*Locustella luscinioides*) that the female does not take part at all. The male of the well-known red-backed shrike (*Lanius collurio*) is not quite so capable. Nevertheless he completes the rough-building of the nest alone, leaving to the female the easier task of titivating the interior.

A bird's nest is usually taken as the symbol of a happy little family which is quite self-contained. In some communal species, however, this symbolic principle has been replaced by a sort of nest socialism. Several couples unite in a common nest-building, and the females then lay all their eggs in this one nest. This is true of a series of exotic birds, the timaliids (*Yuhina bruneiceps*), the South American cuckoo (*Crotophaga*), the white-winged chough (*Cocorax melanorhampus*) and many others. It does not seem to matter if the eggs get mixed up. In the hatching and rearing of the chicks all the parent birds take part in common. This nest socialism does not, however, seem to be a happy solution. In *Crotophaga* it has been observed that such communal nests are deserted if too many eggs have been laid in them. It is, after all, better if each one hatches out its own eggs.

Most birds choose the best-concealed spot for nesting and, in the crowning action of their lives, they seek to avoid all disturbance by man or beast.

Many others, however, find it more agreeable to have company during the time-consuming business of incubating, and join in common breeding colonies, where one nest lies close to the next. The nesting colonies of our rooks or of grey herons show a modest beginning in this. There we may come across a couple of dozen or up to a couple of hundred nests in a wooded meadow, high up in the tree-tops. We hear the croaking from hundreds of throats and see the birds flying, but on the whole such a colony does not present a very imposing spectacle. We get a very different impression on seeing from a distance the nesting colonies of a large sea-bird, say the gannet or the penguin. These birds sit in many thousands close together so that there is nowhere any space between them for a single nest more. Such a breeding colony is a spectacular natural phenomenon.

This holds good also for flamingos, which gather in gigantic swarms in the Rhône Delta in Southern France for breeding purposes. As the stranger approaches the tight mass of thousands of birds, whose brilliant colouring contrasts vividly with the glittering blue of the sea, he is overwhelmed by the spectacle. Only the raucous cries from a thousand throats, which at close quarters rise to a hellish din, mars the spectator's pleasure. If one succeeds in getting near enough he will see that each female has built only a small nest hillock of dried mud in which reposes one, rarely two, chalk-white eggs.

Mammals

In mammals nest-building is confined chiefly to such species as live underground, like moles, or in caves, like foxes. Besides these it is found also in other small mammals, such as mice, squirrels and so on. But in contrast to birds these animals use the nest throughout the year; at the breeding season it is lined with particularly soft material for the benefit of the expected young.

In many cases the provident mother will pluck her abdomen quite bare for this purpose. When the domestic rabbit does this we know that a birth is imminent. The vixen is said to start this hair-plucking as early as the beginning of gestation. Starting at the throat, she continues to do this during the whole period of gestation. This action by the mother serves a double purpose for the young. In the first place they lie soft, and secondly they are able to find the teats more easily on the bare abdomen.

Frequently special safeguards are provided in the breeding nests which are absent from the normal nest. The breeding nest of the hamster is furnished with many exits; the vixen makes several nests and in the end moves into that which has been least disturbed. Rabbits are said to build special nests, known as "stops", in which to have their young. Every time the doe leaves the stop she scrapes earth over the opening and obliterates all sign of an entrance.

Among our native mammals the squirrel may well be said to build the most perfect nest. Experts distinguish four different nests: refuge nests, emergency nests, chief or principal nests and larder nests. Our interest here is only with the principal nest, in which the young are brought into the world. It is always to be found in the fork of a tree, so that wind may not shake it, or in a hollow tree, at times even on the ground. The principal nest is often of considerable size. It may be eighteen inches long and equally broad; the inner cavity is given as about a foot across. It is extraordinarily well padded. It has happened that one such nest, believed to be empty, was flung from a tree to the ground, and neither it nor the young ones came to any harm. The most remarkable thing about this nest is that it has a flap which is of a firm wickerwork and serves as a door. We may say with confidence that no bird makes anything like it. The animals have to use their claws to open this semicircular flap when they want to slip in, and the same to close it behind them.

Some mice also are great artists in nest-building. The house mouse is not outstanding in this. It sets its nest in any old corner and uses anything that comes to hand: wool, hair, rags and so on.

The harvest mouse is a special artist. It has been stated that its nest rivals in beauty that of the birds. It reminds one a little of that of the reed-warbler, and like it is frequently built between reed stems. It is approximately the size of a goose egg. The outer envelope consists of split rushes or the leaves of reeds. The creature draws each leaf carefully through its mouth and slits it with the razor-sharp edges of its teeth. Having subdivided the leaf into six or eight parts in this manner, the fibres are plaited together. The interior of the nest is padded with quite soft material: thistledown, catkins, and flower heads of all kinds. Whether it is true that old mothers make more artistic nests than the younger ones may be deferred.

In all these animals it can be readily shown that the nest-building urge depends on the sex hormones, since it changes with the sexual cycle.

16

EGG CLUTCHES OF BIRDS

SINCE we have gone so minutely into the subject of birds' nests, it becomes necessary to pause for a moment to glance inside and consider the eggs. Birds have brought the art of egg-laying to the greatest perfection. This is evident primarily in that the quantity they lay is the smallest that enables them to keep up their numbers. The plaice lays at least 5,000 eggs a year, frogs several hundreds, snakes a few dozen. On the other hand the large birds are content in many cases to lay only one or two. In the normal course of events, and in all animals, all the progeny of one pair of parents except two are, on the average, destroyed before they themselves are sexually mature and capable of reproduction. In this way there is the guarantee that the population of each species year in, year out, will remain the same. If more than two remain, then the population of a species undergoes a steady increase; if less than two, then the species slowly but surely dies out and becomes extinct. The difference between the original number of progeny and the survivors is called the figure of annihilation. For the plaice this figure is extremely high; for birds, on the other hand, it is comparatively low. Primarily this is connected with the fact that birds' eggs are very perfect structures and secondly that birds have achieved two immense advances in contrast to the cold-blooded vertebrates. First, they brood their eggs, that is to say they shorten the period of development of the embryo up to the hatching by their own bodily heat, and secondly they feed the young until they are capable of feeding themselves.

As to the number of eggs, in general the large birds lay fewer eggs than the small ones. Species laying only one egg each year include, for

PLATE XXIII.

A pair of Macropods, paradise fish, with foam nest.

Deposit of ova of a *Trogulus* spider inside a snail-shell.

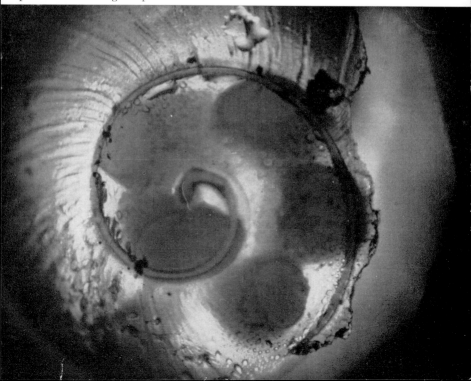

Plate XXIV.
Chimney swallow feeding its young.

example, the large birds of prey, the mighty albatross, the auk and others. Actually the small number of eggs is compensated to a certain extent by the animal's longevity, which is considerably greater in large birds than in small. If the eagle lays one egg every year and repeats this for thirty years or even more then it produces indeed thirty eggs during its lifetime, of which number twenty-eight can perish without diminishing the species. The small birds, our song-birds for instance, lay as a rule many more eggs. This is common knowledge to anyone who has found a clutch of eggs of one of these little birds in the spring, hidden in a thicket. At the same time, however, they do not lay too many. If this were so the sparrows would have picked our cornfields bare long ago. Here therefore care also is taken that, to use a simile, the trees do not reach the sky. The annihilation figure in small birds is much greater than in eagles; the magpie ransacks a nest and enjoys a feed of new-laid eggs, the wicked cat slinks about and seizes the still clumsy young birds. A thousand dangers lie in wait round every corner for those delicate little beasts. Who, however, dares approach the eagle's eyrie, built as it is at a dizzy height on a crag? Man, it is true, had not been reckoned with by Nature when calculating the annihilation figures, and it would certainly have been much better for the eagle if it had laid four or six eggs. Now, alas, it is too late.

17

INCUBATION

In birds, as everyone knows, nest-building and egg-laying are intimately associated with a further process, namely incubation. Whereas in lizards the sun takes care that the necessary heat flows to the eggs in the bosom of the earth, birds have to assist with their own bodily heat.

Incubation is, however, a difficult art and bristles with problems not apparent at first sight. And yet, on the other hand, how simple is the incubator. Every day so many eggs are put in it and no sooner are the chicks hatched than they are taken out. But in a narrow nest things are quite different, and the saying "There is room for all on earth" cannot be applied here. The eggs are laid successively, one today and one tomorrow. There are therefore no twins or triplets, but one of the eggs has the rights of a first-born and the last must retire modestly to the background. When, then, must the mother commence sitting on her eggs? Some birds begin immediately the first egg is laid, in which case the older chicks have already reached a certain size when the youngest is hatched. There is, however, no rejoicing over the latest little brother or sister. Rather, the rest maltreat it until it perishes, as has been observed in rooks and other birds, or they may cast it out of the nest (see Fig. 65). Some parents even take a hand themselves. In the lammergeyer

FIG. 65. The big one is about to strike again.

and certain eagles the second chick is killed and dismembered before it has seen the light of day.

In birds which lay many eggs the problem of competition between the young is a much more urgent one. Most of them have solved it by delaying the incubation somewhat. Some begin when the laying is half completed, others when it is nearly or quite complete. The oldest eggs are then held back in their development, and thus is the picture created which is seen when looking into a nest with young. All five or six are the same size, all have their beaks wide open and all get the same amount of food.

The sharing of incubation has its own peculiar problems. When the bird is of a solitary species, as is the woodcock or the pheasant where the male departs after mating, the question solves itself, of course. The mother broods all the time and the father, who has long ago gone his own way, simply does not care a hang about all this children business. But most birds, as we have seen, live in a strict monogamy, and then the question of sharing the work has to be taken into account. Now, however, we see how very useful is a regular life based on instincts. The times during which the two parents are to sit are laid down forever to the very hour, as if by order, and in this matter there is no tossing up. There are thus no disputes, as there would most certainly be among human beings in the same situation. The male pigeon (*Columba livia*) broods from ten in the forenoon until half past two in the afternoon, the female for the remaining time. The male black swan (*Chenopsis atrata*) is a trifle more industrious, for he broods from ten to five o'clock. There are, however, cases where the males brood throughout the night. This is said of the African ostrich, who sits on the eggs from five in the evening until eight next morning. This has been related to the colouring of the ostrich couple. The cock ostrich is jet black and is thus less conspicuous in the dark, while the hen is grey and is less easily seen by daylight.

Besides the numerous species in which both sexes share the incubation, there are many others in which the brooding has fallen on one or other of the partners. Naturally the females are in the majority; they brood alone in most songsters, most owls, many birds of prey and others. That the male ever broods alone is at first sight rather astonishing. It occurs chiefly among some archaic species, as in cassowaries, Australian emus and South American rheas and the kiwi or apteryx, which also belongs to this group.

How it comes about in these that the male has undertaken the duty, which is in itself plainly a female concern, cannot readily be understood. Darwin himself had a headache over it when he became acquainted with the rheas, and, as was the habit of this man of genius, enunciated a very plausible hypothesis. He believed that the growth of the eggs in the oviducts in these birds proceeds too slowly for them to be able to get a true clutch by laying one egg after another in the usual way. They therefore leave the nest business to the male, and, playing the vagabond, they lay an egg now in one nest, then in another. Of course, these theories remain unproved. It is obvious that only the males incubate in those birds in which polyandry is the rule, such as phaleropes and painted quails.

When birds relieve each other at the nest they do so with a certain formality and ceremonial which is reminiscent of the changing of the guard. This has been described with great insight by Chapman for the pelican: "The returning bird alights near the nest and, with bill pointed to the zenith, advances slowly, waving its head from side to side. At the same time the sitting bird sticks its bill vertically into the nest, twitches its half-spread wings, and utters a low, husky, gasping *chuck*, the only note I have ever heard issue from the throat of an adult wild Brown Pelican. After five or six wand-like passes of its upraised head, the advancing bird pauses, when both birds, with apparent unconcern, begin to preen their feathers, and a moment later the bird that has been on duty steps from the nest, and the new-comer at once takes its place."

With most birds the relief certainly takes place in a somewhat simpler manner. It also happens that the bird being relieved does not immediately give way and the other must wait a fairly long time for its turn.

The period of incubation varies considerably and depends chiefly on the size of the egg, thus indirectly on the size of the bird. In the large albatross, the giant among sea-birds, who moreover lives in a very cold region, the incubation period amounts to from two to three months. In the ostrich in the heat of Africa, on the other hand, it is only forty-two days. As we know, in a domestic hen it is twenty-one days to the time the chick is hatched. The small song-birds make do with less than fourteen days as a rule; the shortest period noted is that of the white-eye (*Zosterops*), in which it is only ten days.

Among the lower animals and the poikilotherms (cold-blooded animals) which guard their eggs, the mother denies herself all food for many weeks. In birds this is also the case now and then. A male emu has been observed to brood faithfully for sixty days without eating anything at all. In eider-duck a week-long fast has been noted. On the whole, however, this is only possible with large birds. In small birds the rate of metabolism is such that the animals cannot endure a long fast. As a rule, the non-brooding male brings food to the female. There are also very bad husbands who do not bother about their wives during the entire incubation period. The wren is one. In them the female helps herself by rising now and then and quickly picking up something to eat, to return to her eggs immediately. Sometimes these birds do not remain sitting for longer than a quarter of an hour at a time. The eggs can stand this. It does not matter if they experience a slight cooling for a time; it merely retards the process of development. Leaving the nest entails other dangers, however, as we have already seen. The cuckoo could not do her nefarious work were the song-bird to remain constantly in its nest.

A much discussed and very remarkable habit is that of the hornbills. These are "cave-breeders" and the male immures his mate. First they combine to reduce the size of the entrance to the breeding chamber. Then the female slips in to lay the eggs, and during this time the male walls up the entrance, closing the opening until only a narrow slit remains through which the female can stretch out her beak. He thereupon returns regularly to feed his mate and she herself enjoys undisturbed peace in the nest.

18

INSESSORS AND AUTOPHAGOUS BIRDS

ANOTHER phenomenon connected intimately with the length of the incubation period and which reacts again on the instinctive life of the adult bird is the stage of development at which the newly-hatched bird has arrived. If the brooding period is relatively short, as in songsters or woodpeckers, then the young bird emerges as an extremely helpless and

FIG. 66. Insessors and autophagi: (*right*) young snipe; (*left*) young cormorant; both about one day old.

undeveloped being. It is quite naked, blind and barely able to make any movement. We call such chicks insessorial or nidicolous, and the parents are saddled with endless duties, the most important being the feeding of this helpless little one. Should the brooding period be long, however, as is characteristic of domestic hens, ducks and geese, then the newly hatched little creature wears the beginnings of a warm downy coat, is firm on its legs and gazes with clear eyes upon its new world.

We can support this with some figures:

	Weight of chick	Brood period (days)	
Mallard duck	$2\frac{1}{4}$ lb.	26	autophagous
Common raven	$2\frac{1}{2}$ lb.	20-21	insessorial
Teal	10 oz.	23	autophagous
Black woodpecker	10 oz.	13	insessorial
Quail	$1\frac{3}{4}$ oz.	13	autophagous
Blackbird	$3\frac{1}{2}$ oz.	14	insessorial

The autophagous birds have generally larger and more yolky eggs. The mallard duck's egg weighs $1\frac{3}{4}$ oz., that of the equally large common raven only 1 oz. The egg of the teal is, at about 1 oz., nearly three times the weight of that of the equally large black woodpecker. The volume of the yolk of the autophagous birds may amount to 40 per cent. of the whole egg, in insessorials only to some 15–20 per cent.

The autophagous birds cause their parents much less trouble than the insessors. During the first twenty-four hours they subsist, to take the domestic chick as an example, on the yolk store which they still carry about in the stomach. These quite young chicks can then be sent without difficulty over long distances by aircraft, since they need no supplementary food. Later, under the guidance of the hen, they forage for themselves. The most independent of the autophagous birds in the world is the young brush turkey. When the newly hatched chick has worked its way out of the gigantic sand heap which its parents had piled on it, it shakes itself, glances round quickly to detect any potential enemy, and then makes a beeline for the nearest bush country. It is thrown entirely on to its own resources.

It is interesting to note that in mammals a completely parallel development has taken place. It is true that we do not speak of them as insessorial and autophagous, but it would hardly be wrong if we did. The former come into the world quite imperfect: naked, blind and still very helpless, the others are already complete and ready to face anything as soon as they see the light of day. As an example of the first group we may choose the rabbit, for the second the guinea-pig. Here, also, a definite relation exists to the process which may be compared to the incubation period, namely the period of gestation.

The period of gestation depends, exactly as does the incubation period, on the size of the beast. In the mouse it is nineteen days, in the hedgehog thirty-five to forty days, in sheep 150 and in horses 328–345 days. Because of this rule, the animals which bear their young incomplete have a much shorter period of gestation than the others whose young can at once see and run. As a telling example of this relation we should note that the small guinea-pig has as long a period of gestation as a large dog (fifty-eight to seventy-two days).

19

GIANT SNAKE AND DUCKBILL

BEFORE concluding the discussion of brood activities we must consider certain animals which, it is true, do not belong to the birds but nevertheless incubate their eggs by means of their personal warmth. The first instance oddly enough concerns the giant snakes. If we re-examine Fig. 56 where the mother encircles her heap of eggs, we become aware that she is by no means protecting the eggs from shocks and other mechanical damage. The mother snake is truly brooding. Although she belongs to the poikilotherms, she generates a higher temperature in her body during this time. If the ambient air is at a temperature of some 30 degrees C. (86 degrees F.), a temperature of 33·8 degrees C. (about 93 degrees F.) to 34·8 degrees C. (about 95 degrees F.) is generated between the coils of her gigantic body, and this is of great advantage to the eggs and hastens hatching.

The second animal to engage our attention is the remarkable duckbill.

That the duckbills, although they are mammals, lay shell eggs has been known since 1827, and the fact has often been discussed. Here we must mention some details that are not so well known. We are dealing, in fact, with very remarkable eggs. The complete egg capable of fertilization has a yolk of only one tenth of an inch diameter; after fertilization it becomes coated with a very thin layer of albumen and surrounded by a transparent soft cartilaginous shell. The most outstanding difference to a bird's egg, however, consists in that it does not remain so, but undergoes further growth in the uterus, and while at first it had a diameter of some one and a half tenths of an inch its greatest length when laid is six to six and a half tenths of an inch! There can be no doubt that the growth in size of the egg is due to absorption of fluid from the uterus. Upon this, moreover, depends the real growth of the embryo. The egg contains far too little nourishing material within itself to make this growth possible. We must assume, therefore, that the fœtus is nourished to a very considerable degree by a secretion of the walls of the uterus. This being so, it proves that the duckbill, although it lays eggs, behaves basically like a true mammal by nourishing its young within the uterus.

After this scientific hors-d'œuvre, we will briefly discuss the duckbill's breeding habits. It builds a nest of grass and various sorts of leaves in a burrow it has itself dug. There the eggs are laid, and there the young are hatched. The incubation is solely the work of the female, who rolls herself into a ball and presses the eggs against the warm skin of her abdomen with her tail. The duckbill does not possess a brood pouch. The young on hatching are naturally still quite small and at an early stage of development, yet they can move immediately they are free, the reverse of the marsupials.

It is noteworthy that the young animal undergoes a fast during the first few days of its life. The mother does not suckle it at once, which is explained by the milk gland not being ready to function at the time of hatching.

20

FEEDING THE YOUNG

IN most animals that care for their young the parents' interest in their progress comes to a natural end at the latest by about the time they have hatched. This we have learnt of the amphibians which care for their brood or of snakes which protect their eggs with their own bodies. It also happens sometimes that the hatched young remain with their parents or mother for a while and are even looked after by them. This is done by the mouth-brooding fish, the young of which withdraw when danger threatens by re-entering the capacious mouth of their father or mother. But in all these the young must feed themselves.

Only in a fairly small number of animals do the parents regularly feed their offspring. This behaviour is found in some hymenoptera among the insects, in most birds and finally in mammals.

(a) THE FEEDING OF YOUNG INSECTS

In insects we are actually dealing only with an alteration of instincts already present. In most of the solitary wasps the cell is sealed up as soon as sufficient nourishment for a larva has been placed in it. Here then we cannot speak of an actual feeding of the larva. Matters are not very different to what is found in butterflies. The mother deposits the eggs where the young animal can find food. The method is excellent if the year is good and there is plenty of prey. It may make difficulties if there is too little food, and from that the feeding instinct has developed, by which the larvæ remain constantly under the control of the mother. In the solitary wasps we have this in a few special cases only. Thus *Synagris cornuta* utilizes captured caterpillars by first breaking them into smaller portions and then chewing them thoroughly. The feeding of the larvæ is done from mouth to mouth. The insect behaves precisely like any bird feeding its young. The cell is closed only when the larva has grown up. How the mother is aware of this is, for the moment, still a mystery. The solitary wasp *Odynerus tropicalis* also constantly brings fresh food to its larvæ. For this the size of the prey is suited to that of the larva. The same is true for some species of *Bembex*. In bees the continual feeding of the brood, in this case of course with honey, has been observed only in the *Allodape* species. In hymenoptera which form communities or hives, on the contrary, the rule is always to feed their larvæ. While the hive is in its early stages the founder wasp or queen has to care for the cells by herself. Here then we have a true instance of a mother feeding her children. The prey, as a rule other insects or spiders, is carved up, portions such as the gut being in some instances discarded, and the edible portion fed to the larvæ after being thoroughly masticated.

(b) THE FEEDING OF THE YOUNG AMONG VERTEBRATES

In vertebrates, as far as is known at present, it is only among mammals and birds that parents feed their young.

Birds

In birds the feeding is of a different character to that in mammals, since they have first to obtain the food. Small birds, for instance our song-birds, making veritably heroic efforts to appease the eternal hunger of their young, have to be intensively busy. Careful observations of the redstart have shown that the young are fed from 220 to 240 times a day; in the tomtit the number may be as many as 300 to 400. In larger birds which bring larger prey to their young the meals are fewer. The large sea-birds, like the albatross, content themselves with filling the stomach of their single chick well once a day.

Usually both parents take part in feeding the young, even when the incubation has been carried out by only one of them. Occasionally this gives rise to an interesting division of labour. Among diurnal birds of prey it is the task of the male to kill a suitable prey and bring it to the nest. Carving it up and sharing it among the young is the prerogative of the mother. This division of labour is illuminating and reminds one to a certain extent of human conditions. The hunter brings home the hare he has shot, the mother prepares it and dishes it up. If among humans one of the parents is not available, the other can, at a pinch, carry on alone; in birds, on the contrary, which are shackled to their unalterable instincts, such an event becomes a catastrophe for the young birds. "The female marsh-harrier disappeared two days ago from the eyrie. The male alone floats to and fro in the sky above it. The male has brought a leveret. He has added a mouse to it and a bunting. He removes the mouse and the bird again and devours them himself. The female is still invisible. In all the flights on which they would otherwise have gone together, the male sails along alone. He calls and only the chicks reply; they are desperate with hunger. The female remains absent. The male settles on the eyrie beside the young, who beg from him, but the female is missing to tear up the prey. They are offered nothing to seize, since the mother does not return. Today is the third day of her absence, and as it rains towards evening the male must take them under his wings, three live ones and one dead. How hunger tortures the young ones! How they whimper and demand food! How they miss the mother who alone can help them! How they sleep ever longer, squeezed together, the dead little one amongst them! The hours slip away, morning comes again. The sun peeps into the eyrie; every day it had warmed the chicks' pelts. Today its benefit is wasted, for all the little ones are dead." (G. Hoffmann.) The male is thus incapable of undertaking the female's duties notwithstanding that he tears up his own share of the prey. So narrow is instinctive life.

In the mechanics of feeding all sorts of habits have been formed. In our song-birds the food is offered to the young with the beak and stuffed down their wide-open throats. The young gape, as one says (see Plate XXIV). Since it is pretty dark in the nest, however, especially with those nesting in hollows, Nature has supplied special guide marks which show the parents the right direction. The mucous membrane of the mouth cavity is a glaring colour, generally yellow, orange or red. For the rest, the competition of the youngsters amongst themselves is of considerable importance. Through it the weak and less energetic are sorted out. In the bird's nest the word is "he who doesn't ask doesn't want, he who doesn't want has had it". The young nestling which, when the mother comes, does not open its beak thoroughly wide, does not shoulder its way to the edge of the nest and otherwise make itself conspicuous, gets precisely nothing. In those instances in which the chicks are not all fed at once they must queue up, one behind the other. This may be regulated by various instincts in the young birds. Among many insectivores, which have a rapid digestion, each chick, when it has had its share, withdraws discreetly and empties itself at another point over the nest rim. Thus it makes room for its neighbour. In this way the young move about the nest, always in a circle in spite of its narrowness. In some species even the sense of the circular movement is governed by instinct. In kingfishers (*Alcedo atthis*) the nest lies at the end of a long tunnel in a bank and during feeding time complete darkness reigns. Here the young move strictly in rotation to the left, counter-clockwise. As each receives a fish it moves to the left and makes way for its right-hand neighbour, which now claims the next fish. So gradually they all have their turn.

In some birds quite special conditions have developed for feeding the young. Pigeons feed their young at first on the so-called crop milk. At the mating season the lining of the crop begins to proliferate under the action of certain hormones and its cells become gradually transformed into an exceedingly fatty porridge, which of course is not a true milk, but, like it, is exceedingly nourishing. It is especially remarkable that this phenomenon occurs in both sexes. The cock must also collaborate and is active as a provider of milk. In flamingos it has been observed that during the first days, the parents allow a few drops of a clear liquid to flow from their own beaks into that of the young chick. Unfortunately, it is not known either whence these drops come or of what they consist, nor is the significance of this proceeding known, though it clearly is not without importance.

Mammals

The nourishment of the young mammals, so long as they are suckled by the mother, is primarily more a physiological problem, although the correct instinctive behaviour of the mother as well as of the young animal must naturally be presupposed. The young must have the instinct to seek the teats and to find them. The mother must place herself at their disposal at the right time. It is known that in domesticated animals these instincts frequently do not function correctly and the mother denies her children their nourishment. In the first place the male is understandably completely superfluous, and in this we see again the great difference from birds, in which the father can from the start take part in the incubation. The reason for this is rather because in mammals there is seldom a true mating. In many mammals, for instance in foxes and wolves, the females even have the instinct to deny the male access to the lair where the young are being reared. On completion of the suckling period the herbivores and the carnivores behave very differently. In the former the young can immediately feed themselves. The parents, chiefly the mother, only help them when danger threatens, either by defending them or by a timely warning. In carnivores, on the other hand, the young, even when they are no longer drinking milk, must be fed at first by the parent, since they are still too weak and inexperienced to provide themselves with the necessary prey. Here, also, a great contrast between bird and mammal shows itself. The bird is the perfect instinctive animal; in mammals many instincts indeed are present, it is true, but the animal cannot live by them alone, and experience must also contribute. The young must then first learn how to catch their prey. The vixen therefore very soon brings her young small live animals so that they may learn how to seize and kill them. After some weeks they can accompany the mother in the hunt, and after some months they will at last have got so far that they are able to risk going alone. In foxes and wolves and probably many other beasts of prey, the father, as soon as the young are weaned, busies himself with feeding the family. The same has also been observed in lions. He it is that drags the prey to the family camping site.

Parental guidance

Besides the feeding of the young the most important task for the parents amongst warm-blooded animals is their guidance. We distinguish between parent families, mother families and father families, according to which becomes the leader. The grey geese form a parent family; father, mother and children remain together until, in the following spring, the parents proceed to have a new brood. Mother families are found in domestic poultry and all birds living solitary lives, also deer and wild pigs, badgers and bears. An example of the father family is furnished by the South American rheas. How matters progress in such families we know best from the domestic hen. We may well draw inferences from them on the behaviour of most of the other warm-blooded animals.

First, what is a clucker? By no means every adult hen but only one who has just completed three weeks' sitting on the nest and has hatched out her eggs. Only after this act do the maternal instincts awaken in her. The leadership of the clucking hen is a difficult post and by no means consists only of running in front of the chicks. Rather it is her task to introduce the little ones to life. The poultry-breeder knows that there are good and bad cluckers; some achieve great fame.

The clucker has all sorts of things to do. Let us commence with the protective function. Here there is among cluckers every shade of behaviour from furious onslaughts against every imagined opponent to the cautious withdrawal of the chicks out of the danger zone. This sort of protective instinct is probably present in all warm-blooded animals. Even a weak song-bird defends its young like a lioness. The hind, not normally a heroine, defends her fawn against the fox. Brückner, from whom most of the foregoing is extracted, describes a personal incident: "The fox passed within thirty yards to one side of the hind, along a ditch. The hind never took her eyes off him. Her attitude was tense and several times she stamped impatiently with her forefeet. This did not, however, pass unnoticed by the fox; on the contrary he glanced ever towards his adversary so as not to be taken by surprise. Suddenly she shot towards him full of fury, whilst he ducked and tried to hide himself in the tall weeds. In a trice she stood over him, beat a tattoo on him with her horn-shod feet; now he streaked off in wild flight, followed for some minutes by the infuriated old beast, who then returned to her fawn, which had waited, frozen on the spot." That it is better to avoid sows with young piglets is very well known.

The clucker's communication with her chicks is represented by her enticing call, which can be greatly modulated. She has a special call when she has found something succulent, and on receipt of it all the chicks come running towards her swiftly. She has another when danger is imminent and yet another when she threatens an opponent. When she has found something palatable she holds it up with repeated inviting calls and motions of her head. She scratches earthworms out of the ground and points them out to the chicks. Her attitude towards a strange chick is very characteristic: "With ruffled plumage, widespread wings, and fanned-out tail she swoops down on it with loud threatening cries and hacks it to pieces if it does not beat a timely retreat."

Since she can make this distinction between her own and strange chicks we can easily conclude that the clucker knows her own chicks to a certain extent personally. How little we can apply human standards to this is shown by the following experiment. If one removes a whole lot of chicks one by one from a clucker without being seen, it makes no impression on her. But should one remove all the chicks she can no longer satisfy her "cluck urge" and she will then show in her whole demeanour that an essential part of her life has been taken away.

The chicks for their part know the clucker personally, and can distinguish her without hesitation from all other hens, even from those of her own breed. They know her own individual call. This family, which seems to be so united by many interests on both sides, breaks up after a few weeks. This is not only true of the domestic fowl but also of all the families of warm-blooded animals. The clucker drives her chicks away with hard blows of her beak when they are seven to eight weeks old. At first they do not understand, but are soon brought to know better by further blows and depart. The large birds of prey, hawks and eagles, do not tolerate their own young in their own territory after they are fledged, and drive them off by force. In some cases the break-up of the family is due to the young emancipating themselves from their mother. Brehm writes of the goosander that at first the young gather round the mother after every expedition. Gradually they keep away from her oftener and form a social community amongst themselves, until eventually each bird goes its own way.

Man forms an exception even in his care of the young. This time it is a laudable one. He provides for his offspring until they are twenty or even twenty-five years old, indeed even for his grandchildren. But the dispersal of the family which we have just found cannot be prevented thereby. It is caused by emancipation. One day the young fly away and the old remain lonely behind.

> "The grown-up children break away
> As easily as in October days
> The apples, without breath of air,
> Part from the twig and on the warm turf fall.
>
> "The lovely bloom which we protect with joy
> And with a happy glance see ripen into fruit
> Within now stirs the browning seed
> And seeks to rid itself for ever of our care.
>
> "It yearns for earth and also for the sun
> Yearns for the sunset and the sunrise too.
> And we stand lonely there—and solemnly
> The autumn wind blows through the leaves."

(Münchhausen from Brückner.)